MULTICULTURE
PROJECTS INDEX

# Clever Cooks

## A CONCOCTION OF STORIES, CHARMS, RECIPES AND RIDDLES

ILLUSTRATED BY
# Trina Schart Hyman

# CLEVER COOKS

## A CONCOCTION OF
## STORIES, CHARMS, RECIPES
## AND RIDDLES

COMPILED BY Ellin Greene

LOTHROP, LEE & SHEPARD COMPANY
NEW YORK

*Retellings by Ellin Greene*

\* \* \*

THE PUMPKIN GIANT
by Mary E. Wilkins
Illustrated by Trina Schart Hyman

PRINCESS ROSETTA
AND THE POPCORN MAN
by Mary E. Wilkins
Illustrated by Trina Schart Hyman

# ❧ | ACKNOWLEDGMENTS

"The Woman Who Flummoxed the Fairies" from *Heather and Broom* by Sorche Nic Leodhas. Copyright © 1960 by Leclair G. Alger. Reprinted by permission of Holt, Rinehart and Winston, Inc.

"Brewery of Eggshells" is from *Celtic Fairy Tales* by Joseph Jacobs. G. P. Putnam's Sons, n.d.

"The Old Woman Who Lost Her Dumpling" is from *Japanese Fairy Tale Series No. 24* rendered into English by Lafcadio Hearn. T. Hasegawa, 1902.

"Clever Oonagh" from *Fairy Tales from the British Isles* by Amabel Williams-Ellis.

"Pinto Smalto" is from *Il Pentamerone* by Giovanni Bastiste Basile. Translated from the Italian of Benedetto Croce (1891) by Martha Lucci and retold by the compiler.

"The Miller, Mis Cook and the King." Reprinted by permission of The World Publishing Company from *The Golden Bird: Folk Tales from Slovenia* by Vladimir Kavcic. Translation Copyright © 1969 by The World Publishing Company.

"Dwarf Long Nose" is from *Violet Fairy Book* by Andrew Lang. Longmans, Green and Company, Inc., 1901.

"Clever Grethel" from *Tales Told Again* by Walter de la Mare. Copyright © 1927 and renewed 1955 by Walter de la Mare. Reprinted by permission of Alfred A. Knopf, Inc.

"The One-Legged Crane." Copyright © 1958 by Domenico Vittorini. From the book *Old Italian Tales* published by David McKay Company, Inc. Reprinted by permission of the publisher.

"The Birth of Simnel Cake" and "Menu for a King" are from *The New Book of Days,* by Eleanor Farjeon. Used by permission of Henry Z. Walck, Inc.

"The Perambulatin' Pumpkin" from *Tall Tales from the High Hills* by Ellis Credle, copyright © 1957. Reprinted by permission of the publisher, Thomas Nelson Inc.

"The Old Woman and the Tramp" is retold by the compiler from *Fairy Tales from the Swedish* by Nils Gabriel Djurklou, translated by H. L. Braekstad. F. A. Stokes, 1901.

Charms and riddles are from Oral Tradition and are taken from the following printed sources: *The Nursery Rhymes of England* by James Halliwell and *English Riddles from Oral Tradition* by Archer Taylor.

The compiler wishes to thank the many people who have had a part in this book: the boys and girls who shared the pleasure of these tales, the folklorists who have preserved the traditions and customs associated with food, and family and friends who contributed recipes and sampled results.

*For my niece, Jeanne, who helped test the recipes*

# Contents

Foreword | 11

The Woman Who Flummoxed the Fairies | 13

Fairy Cake Recipe | 25

Come, butter, come | 26

Butter Cookies Recipe | 27

Brewery of Eggshells | 28

The Old Woman Who Lost Her Dumpling | 32

Cherry Dumpling Recipe | 39

Clever Oonagh | 41

Griddle Bread Recipe | 55

Dwarf Long Nose | 56

Chocolate Potato Cake | 87

Chocolate Butter Icing | 88

Cushy cow, bonny | 89

Molasses Milk Shake Recipe | 89

Pinto Smalto | 90

Marzipan Recipe | 98

Coconut Kisses | 100

The Miller, His Cook and the King | 101

Menu for a King | 108

Clever Grethel | 109

Roast Chicken Recipe | 115

The One-Legged Crane | 117

A Very Great Curiosity | 124

Pancake Day | 125

Pancake Recipes | 127-128

Honey Butter Recipe | 129

The Birth of Simnel Cake | 130

Simnel Cake Recipe | 134

The Perambulatin' Pumpkin | 137

Pumpkin Chiffon Pie Recipe | 143

Gingersnap Crumb Crust Recipe | 144

The Old Woman and the Tramp | 145

Hearty Soup Recipe | 153

Index of Recipes | 155

# Foreword

**M**ost of the stories in this book are about master cooks or bakers who get themselves into trouble through their culinary skills but their quick wits—and sometimes a bit of magic—get them out.

Sandwiched in between the stories are recipes, charms, and a few riddles to test *your* wits. Here's a hint—the correct answer to each riddle is something to eat.

# The Woman Who Flummoxed The Fairies

There was a woman once who was a master baker. Her bannocks were like wheaten cakes, her wheaten cakes were like the finest pastries, and her pastries were like nothing but Heaven itself in the mouth!

Not having her match, or anything like it, in seven counties round she made a good penny by it, for there wasn't a wedding nor a christening for miles around in the countryside but she was called upon to make the cakes for it, and she got all the trade of all the gentry as well. She was fair in her prices and she was honest, too, but she was that good-hearted into the bargain. Those who could pay well she charged aplenty, but when some poor body came and begged her to make a wee bit of a cake for a celebration and timidly offered her the little money they had for it, she'd wave it away and tell them to pay her when they got the cake. Then she'd set to and bake a cake as fine and big as any she'd make for a laird, and she'd send it to them as a gift, with the best respects of her husband and herself, to the wedding pair or the parents of the baby that was to be christened, so nobody's feelings were hurt.

Not only was she a master baker, but she was the cleverest woman in the world; and it was the first that got her into trouble, but it was the second that got her out of it.

The fairies have their own good foods to eat, but they dearly love a bit of baker's cake once in a while, and will often steal a slice of one by night from a kitchen while all the folks in a house are sleeping.

In a nearby hill there was a place where the fairies lived, and of all cakes the ones the fairies like best were the ones this master baker made. The trouble was, the taste of one was hard to come by, for her cakes were all so good that they were always eaten up at a sitting, with hardly a crumb left over for a poor fairy to find.

So then the fairies plotted together to carry the woman away and to keep her with them always just to bake cakes for them.

Their chance came not long after, for there was to be a great wedding at the castle with hundreds of guests invited, and the woman was to make the cakes. There would have to be so many of them, with so many people coming to eat them, that the woman was to spend the whole day before the wedding in the castle kitchen doing nothing but bake one cake after another!

The fairies learned about this from one of their number who had been listening at the keyhole of the baker's door. They found out, too, what road she'd be taking coming home.

When the night came, there they were by a fairy mound where the road went by, hiding in flower cups, and under leaves, and in all manner of places.

When she came by they all flew out at her. "The fireflies are gey thick the night," said she. But it was not fireflies. It was fairies with the moonlight sparkling on their wings.

Then the fairies drifted fern seed into her eyes, and all of a sudden she was that sleepy that she could go not one step farther without a bit of a rest!

"Mercy me!" she said with a yawn. "It's worn myself out I have this day!" And she sank down on what she took to be a grassy bank to doze just for a minute. But it wasn't a bank at all. It was the fairy mound, and once she lay upon it she was in the fairies' power.

She knew nothing about that nor anything else till she woke again, and found herself in fairyland. Being a clever woman she didn't have to be told where she was, and she guessed how she got there. But she didn't let on.

"Well now," she said happily, "and did you ever! It's all my life I've wanted to get a peep into fairyland. And here I am!"

They told her what they wanted, and she said to herself indeed she had no notion of staying there the rest of her life! But she didn't tell the fairies that either.

"To be sure!" she said cheerfully. "Why you poor wee things! To think of me baking cakes for everyone else, and not a one for you! So let's be at it," said she, "with no time wasted."

Then from her kittiebag that hung at her side she took a clean apron and tied it around her waist, while the fairies, happy that she was so willing, licked their lips in anticipation and rubbed their hands for joy.

"Let me see now," said she, looking about her.

"Well, 'tis plain you have nothing for me to be baking a cake with. You'll just have to be going to my own kitchen to fetch back what I'll need."

Yes, the fairies could do that. So she sent some for eggs, and some for sugar, and some for flour, and some for butter, while others flew off to get a wheen of other things she told them she had to have. At last all was ready for the mixing and the woman asked for a bowl. But the biggest one they could find for her was the size of a teacup, and a wee dainty one at that.

Well then, there was nothing for it, but they must go and fetch her big yellow crockery bowl from off the shelf over the water butt. And after that it was her wooden spoons and her egg whisp and one thing and another, till the fairies were all fagged out, what with the flying back and forth, and the carrying, and only the thought of the cake to come of it kept their spirits up at all.

At last everything she wanted was at hand. The woman began to measure and mix and whip and beat. But all of a sudden she stopped.

" 'Tis no use!" she sighed. "I can't ever seem to mix a cake without my cat beside me, purring."

"Fetch the cat!" said the fairy king sharply.

So they fetched the cat. The cat lay at the woman's feet and purred, and the woman stirred away at the bowl, and for a while all was well. But not for long.

The woman let go of the spoon and sighed again. "Well now, would you think it?" said she. "I'm that used to my dog setting the time of my beating by the way he snores at every second beat that I can't seem to get the beat right without him."

"Fetch the dog!" cried the king.

So they fetched the dog and he curled up at her feet beside the cat. The dog snored, the cat purred, the woman beat the cake batter, and all was well again. Or so the fairies thought.

But no! The woman stopped again. "I'm that worried about my babe," said she. "Away from him all night as I've been, and him with a new tooth pushing through this very week. It seems I just can't mix . . ."

"Fetch that babe!" roared the fairy king, without waiting for her to finish what she was saying. And they fetched the babe.

So the woman began to beat the batter again. But when they brought the babe, he began to scream the minute he saw her, for he was hungry, as she knew he would be, because he never would let his dadda feed him his porridge and she had not been home to do it.

"I'm sorry to trouble you," said the woman, raising her voice above the screaming of the babe, "but I can't stop beating now lest the cake go wrong. Happen my husband could get the babe quiet if . . ."

The fairies didn't wait for the king to tell them what to do. Off they flew and fetched the husband back with them. He, poor man, was all in a whirl, what with things disappearing from under his eyes right and left, and then being snatched through the air himself the way he was. But here was his wife, and he knew where she was things couldn't go far wrong. But the baby went on screaming.

So the woman beat the batter, and the baby screamed, and the cat purred, and the dog snored, and the man rubbed his eyes and watched his wife to see what she was up to. The fairies settled down, though 'twas plain to see that the babe's screaming disturbed them. Still, they looked hopeful.

Then the woman reached over and took up the egg whisp and gave the wooden spoon to the babe, who at once began to bang away with it, screaming just the same. Under cover of the screaming of the babe and the banging of the spoon and the swishing of the egg whisp the woman whispered to her husband, "Pinch the dog!"

"What?" said the man. But he did it just the same —and kept on doing it.

"Tow! ROW! ROW!" barked the dog, and added his voice to the babe's screams, and the banging of the wooden spoon, and the swishing of the egg whisp.

"Tread on the tail of the cat!" whispered the woman to her husband, and it's a wonder he could hear her. But he did. He had got the notion now and he entered the game for himself. He not only trod on the tail of the cat, but he kept his foot there

while the cat howled like a dozen lost souls.

So the woman swished, and the baby screamed, and the wooden spoon banged, and the dog yelped, and the cat howled, and the whole of it made a terrible din. The fairies, king and all, flew round and round in distraction with their hands over their ears, for if there is one thing the fairies can't bear it's a lot of noise and there was a lot more than a lot of noise in fairyland that day! And what's more the woman knew what they liked and what they didn't all the time!

So then the woman got up and poured the batter into two pans that stood ready. She laid by the egg whisp and took the wooden spoon away from the babe, and picking him up she popped a lump of sugar into his mouth. That surprised him so much that he stopped screaming. She nodded to her husband and he stopped pinching the dog and took his foot from the cat's tail, and in a minute's time all was quiet. The fairies stopped flying round and round and sank down exhausted.

And then the woman said, "The cake's ready for the baking. Where's the oven?"

The fairies looked at each other in dismay, and at last the fairy queen said weakly, "There isn't any oven."

"What!" exclaimed the woman. "No oven? Well then, how do you expect me to be baking the cake?"

None of the fairies could find the answer to that.

"Well then," said the woman, "you'll just have to be taking me and the cake home to bake it in my own oven, and bring me back later when the cake's all done."

The fairies looked at the babe and the wooden spoon and the egg whisp and the dog and the cat and the man. And then they all shuddered like one.

"You may all go!" said the fairy king. "But don't ask us to be taking you. We're all too tired."

"Och, you must have your cake then," said the woman, feeling sorry for them now she'd got what she wanted, which was to go back to her own home, "after all the trouble you've had for it! I'll tell you what I'll do. After it's baked, I'll be leaving it for you beside the road, behind the bank where you found me. And what's more I'll put one there for you every single week's end from now on."

The thought of having one of the woman's cakes every week revived the fairies so that they forgot they were all worn out. Or almost did.

"I'll not be outdone!" cried the fairy king. "For what you find in that same place shall be your own!"

Then the woman picked up the pans of batter,

and the man tucked the bowls and spoons and things under one arm and the baby under the other. The fairy king raised an arm and the hill split open. Out they all walked, the woman with the pans of batter, the man with the bowls and the babe, and the dog and the cat at their heels. Down the road they walked and back to their own house, and never looked behind them.

When they got back to their home the woman put the pans of batter into the oven, and then she dished out the porridge that stood keeping hot on the back of the fire and gave the babe his supper.

There wasn't a sound in that house except for the clock ticking and the kettle singing and the cat purring and the dog snoring. And all those were soft, quiet sounds.

"I'll tell you what," said the man at last. "It doesn't seem fair on the rest of the men that I should have the master baker and the cleverest woman in the world all in one wife."

"Trade me off then for one of the ordinary kind," said his wife, laughing at him.

"I'll not do it," said he. "I'm very well suited as I am."

So that's the way the woman flummoxed the fairies. A good thing she made out of it, too, for when the cake was baked and cooled the woman took it up and put it behind the fairy mound, as she had promised. And when she set it down she saw there a little brown bag. She took the bag up and opened it and looked within, and it was full of bright shining yellow gold pieces.

And so it went, week after week. A cake for the fairies, a bag of gold for the woman and her husband. They never saw one of the fairies again, but the bargain never was broken and they grew rich by it. So of course they lived, as why should they not, happily ever after.

1 cup (2 sticks) butter
  at room temperature
2 cups sugar
4 eggs
3 cups sifted flour
3 teaspoons baking powder
⅛ teaspoon salt
1 cup milk
1 teaspoon vanilla

Jam
Shredded coconut

Butter and flour a 10-inch tube pan.

Cream the butter and sugar until light and fluffy. Beat in the eggs, one at a time.

Sift the flour with the baking powder and salt, and add it alternately with the milk. Begin and end with the flour to make a cake of fine texture.

Beat for at least 3 minutes, or until the mixture is well-blended. Stir in vanilla.

Pour into buttered and floured tube pan.

Bake in a 350° F. oven for about an hour. To test doneness, insert a toothpick or cake tester in cake an inch from either side. When it comes out clean, the cake is done.

Let cool about 30 minutes in the pan before turning out on a rack to finish cooling.

When cool, spread your favorite jam over the top and sprinkle with coconut. This cake also tastes good served plain or sprinkled with powdered sugar.

*Come, butter, come,*
*Come, butter, come;*
*Peter stands at the gate*
*Waiting for a butter cake.*
*Come, butter, come.*

This charm was repeated over the churn when the butter was slow in forming. It is centuries old and goes back to the time when people believed that the fairies had got into the churn when the cream would not clot. "Peter" probably refers to Saint Peter.

1 cup (2 sticks) butter at room temperature
⅔ cup light brown sugar
1 egg yolk
2 cups sifted flour
¼ teaspoon baking powder
1 teaspoon vanilla

In a large bowl cream butter until soft and smooth. Add sugar. Beat in egg yolk. Sift flour with baking powder and add gradually, stirring after each addition until thoroughly blended. Stir in vanilla. Drop by teaspoons on ungreased cookie sheet. Bake at 300° F. until lightly browned (about 20 minutes). Makes about 5 dozen cookies.

\* \* \*

*A riddle, a riddle,*
*A hole in the middle.*

A doughnut

# Brewery of Eggshells

*In medieval days people believed that fairies and other supernatural beings might seize and carry off newborn babies and leave in their place one of themselves. The changeling, or change-child, must be forced to betray himself in speech or action. Of all the devices used, the most common one was cooking something in an eggshell. The purpose was to so arouse the changeling's curiosity that he would reveal his ancient age.*

In Treneglwys there is a certain shepherd's cot known by the name of Twt y Cymrws because of the strange strife that occurred there. There once lived there a man and his wife, and they had twins whom the woman nursed tenderly. One day she was called away to the house of a neighbor at some distance. She did not much like going and leaving her little ones all alone in a solitary house, especially as she had heard tell of the good folk haunting the neighborhood.

Well, she went and came back as soon as she could, but on her way back she was frightened to see some goblins of the blue petticoat crossing her path though it was midday. She rushed home, but found her two little ones in the cradle and everything seemed as it was before.

But after a time the man and his wife began to suspect that something was wrong, for the twins didn't grow at all.

The man said: "They're not ours."

The woman said: "Whose else should they be?"

And so arose the great strife so that the neighbors named the cottage after it. It made the woman very sad, so one evening she made up her mind to go and see the Wise Man of Llanidloes, for he knew everything and would advise her what to do.

So she went to Llanidloes and told the case to the Wise Man. Now there was soon to be a harvest of rye and oats, so the Wise Man said to her, "When you are getting dinner for the reapers, clear out the shell of a hen's egg and boil some pottage in it, and then take it to the door as if you meant it as a dinner

for the reapers. Then listen if the twins say anything. If you hear them speaking of things beyond
the understanding of children, go back and take
them up and throw them into the waters of Lake
Elvyn. But if you don't hear anything remarkable,
do them no injury."

So when the day of the reap came the woman did
all that the Wise Man ordered, and put the eggshell

on the fire and took it off and carried it to the door, and there she stood and listened. Then she heard one of the children say to the other:

> *Acorn before oak I knew,*
> *An egg before a hen,*
> *But I never heard of an eggshell brew*
> *A dinner for harvest men.*

So she went back into the house, seized the children and threw them into the Llyn, and the goblins in their blue trousers came and saved their children and the mother had her own children back and so the great strife ended.

\* \* \*

> *In marble halls as white as milk,*
> *Lined with a skin as soft as silk,*
> *Within a fountain crystal clear,*
> *A golden apple doth appear.*
> *No doors there are to this stronghold,*
> *Yet thieves break in and steal the gold.*

An egg.

# The Old Woman
# Who Lost Her Dumpling

*An* Oni *is an ogre.* Jizō *is the Japanese guardian deity of children and travelers.*

Long, long ago there was a funny old woman, who liked to laugh and to make dumplings of rice-flour.

One day, while she was preparing some dumplings for dinner, she let one fall; and it rolled into a hole in the earthen floor of her little kitchen and disappeared. The old woman tried to reach it by putting her hand down the hole, and all at once the earth gave way, and the old woman fell in.

She fell quite a distance, but was not a bit hurt; and when she got up on her feet again, she saw that she was standing on a road, just like the road before her house. It was quite light down there; and she could see plenty of rice fields, but no one in them. How all this happened, I cannot tell you. But it seems that the old woman had fallen into another country.

The road she had fallen upon sloped very much; so, after having looked for her dumpling in vain, she thought that it must have rolled farther away down the slope. She ran down the road to look, crying:

"My dumpling, my dumpling! Where is that dumpling of mine?"

After a little while she saw a stone *Jizō* standing by the roadside, and she said:

"O Lord *Jizō*, did you see my dumpling?"

*Jizō* answered:

"Yes, I saw your dumpling rolling by me down the road. But you had better not go any farther, because there is a wicked *Oni* living down there, who eats people."

But the old woman only laughed, and ran on farther down the road, crying: "My dumpling, my dumpling! Where is that dumpling of mine?" And she came to another statue of *Jizō*, and asked it:

"O kind Lord *Jizō*, did you see my dumpling?"

And *Jizō* said:

"Yes, I saw your dumpling go by a little while

ago. But you must not run any farther, because there is a wicked *Oni* down there, who eats people."

But she only laughed, and ran on, still crying out: "My dumpling, my dumpling! Where is that dumpling of mine?" And she came to a third *Jizō*, and asked it:

"O dear Lord *Jizō*, did you see my dumpling?"

But *Jizō* said:

"Don't talk about your dumpling now. Here is the *Oni* coming. Squat down here behind my sleeve, and don't make any noise."

Presently the *Oni* came very close, and stopped and bowed to *Jizō*, and said:

"Good-day, *Jizō San!*"

*Jizō* said good-day, too, very politely.

Then the *Oni* suddenly snuffed the air two or three times in a suspicious way, and cried out: "*Jizō San, Jizō San!* I smell a smell of mankind somewhere—don't you?"

"Oh!" said *Jizō*, "perhaps you are mistaken."

"No, no!" said the *Oni* after snuffing the air again, "I smell a smell of mankind."

Then the old woman could not help laughing— "*Te-he-he!*"—and the *Oni* immediately reached down his big hairy hand behind *Jizō's* sleeve, and pulled her out, still laughing, "*Te-he-he!*"

"Ah! ha!" cried the *Oni*.

Then *Jizō* said:

"What are you going to do with that good old woman? You must not hurt her."

"I won't," said the *Oni*. "But I will take her home with me to cook for us."

"*Te-he-he!*" laughed the old woman.

"Very well," said *Jizō*; "but you must really be kind to her. If you are not, I shall be very angry."

"I won't hurt her at all," promised the *Oni*; "and she will only have to do a little work for us every day. Good-by, *Jizō San*."

Then the *Oni* took the old woman far down the road, till they came to a wide deep river, where there was a boat. He put her into the boat, and took her across the river to his house. It was a very large house. He led her at once into the kitchen, and told her to cook some dinner for himself and the other *Oni* who lived with him. And he gave her a small wooden rice-paddle, and said:

"You must always put only one grain of rice into the pot, and when you stir that one grain of rice in the water with this paddle, the grain will multiply until the pot is full."

So the old woman put just one rice grain into the pot, as the *Oni* told her, and began to stir it with

the paddle; and, as she stirred, the one grain became two—then four—then eight—then sixteen, thirty-two, sixty-four, and so on. Every time she moved the paddle the rice increased in quantity; and in a few minutes the great pot was full.

After that, the funny old woman stayed a long time in the house of the *Oni*, and every day cooked food for him and for all his friends. The *Oni* never hurt or frightened her, and her work was made quite easy by the magic paddle—although she had to cook a very, very great quantity of rice, because an *Oni* eats much more than any human being eats.

But she felt lonely, and always wished very much to go back to her own little house, and make her dumplings. And one day, when the *Oni* were all out somewhere, she thought she would try to run away.

She first took the magic paddle, and slipped it under her girdle; and then she went down to the river. No one saw her; and the boat was there. She got into it, and pushed off; and as she could row very well, she was soon far away from the shore.

But the river was very wide; and she had not rowed more than one-fourth of the way across, when the *Oni*, all of them, came back to the house.

They found that their cook was gone, and the magic paddle, too. They ran down to the river at once, and saw the old woman rowing away very fast.

Perhaps they could not swim; at all events they had no boat; and they thought the only way they could catch the funny old woman would be to drink up all the water of the river before she got to the other bank. So they knelt down, and began to drink so fast that before the old woman had got half way over, the water had become quite low.

But the old woman kept on rowing until the water had got so shallow that the *Oni* stopped drinking, and began to wade across. Then she dropped her oar, took the magic paddle from her girdle, and shook it at the *Oni*, and made such funny faces that the *Oni* all burst out laughing.

But the moment they laughed, they could not help throwing up all the water they had drunk, and so the river became full again. The *Oni* could not cross, and the funny old woman got safely over to the other side, and ran away up the road as fast as she could.

She never stopped running until she found herself at home again.

After that she was very happy, for she could make dumplings whenever she pleased. Besides, she had the magic paddle to make rice for her. She sold her dumplings to her neighbors and passengers, and in quite a short time she became rich.

*Rice flour is a fine white flour milled from rice. The recipe below calls for cake flour.*

## CHERRY DUMPLINGS

2 cups (1 pound can) pitted red sour cherries
¾ cup sugar
1 tablespoon quick-cooking tapioca
1 cup sifted cake flour
1 teaspoon baking powder
¼ teaspoon salt
Grated rind of 1 orange if desired
⅓ cup milk
2 teaspoons butter, melted

Pour undrained cherries into a large, deep skillet. Add ½ cup sugar. Sprinkle with tapioca. Let stand while preparing dumpling dough.

Sift ¼ cup sugar, flour, baking powder and salt. Add remaining ingredients and mix lightly.

Bring cherry mixture to a boil. Drop dumpling dough from a tablespoon into boiling mixture, making 6 dumplings. Cover skillet and cook gently 20 minutes. Serve warm with milk or cream if desired.

*Come riddle, come riddle my roe-tee-tee-tote,*
*A little red man in a little red coat,*
*A stone in his belly, a stick in his throat,*
*Come tell me this riddle, and I'll give you a groat.*

A cherry in a tree

*A groat was an old English coin.*

# Clever Oonagh

There was once a giant in Ireland called Cucul-lin, and another giant that was also supposed to be a mighty warrior, though he wasn't near so big. His name was Fin.

There's many a terrible tale told about these two—Cucullin and Fin—and their great and famous deeds and their battles. But there's one story about them and about Fin's wife Oonagh which is different. Maybe it's just a tale that was told round about the country by those who were sick and tired of hearing only about their killing and slaughtering and the great deeds. Perhap a few people wanted to have the laugh of them.

Now Fin had his house at the very top of a steep hill called Knockmany, which wasn't really just such a very convenient place for a house, because, you see, whichever way the wind blew, it always blew up there. Another thing was that, when her husband Fin was away, Oonagh had always to go down to the very bottom of the steep hill to the spring before she could draw a drop of water, and then she had to carry her full pails all the way to the top again.

But all the same 'twas a good spot for a house in one way, for being perched up like that at the very top of Knockmany Hill, Fin could see all ways—North, South, East and West—and that gave him a good warning if any of his enemies should take it into their heads to pay him a visit. Fin wasn't one to like being taken by surprise. He had yet another way of getting a warning, as well as keeping a good look-out. He would put his thumb into his mouth till it touched one special tooth, right at the back, and then the thumb would tell him what was coming to pass.

Well, one day, when all seemed peaceful, Fin was sitting with his wife, Oonagh, when she saw that he had put his thumb in his mouth.

'What are you doing that for, Fin?' says she.

'Oh, my grief and sorrow, he's coming!' said Fin as soon as he had pulled out his thumb and could speak plain, and she saw that he looked as miserable as a wet Sunday.

'Who's coming?' asked Oonagh.

'That horrid beast of an old Cucullin, no less,' answered Fin.

Now, as Oonagh well knew, though Fin was near as tall and big as a round-tower, Cucullin was bigger still and was an enemy that Fin didn't want to meet, no not for all the world. All the giants for miles around were afraid of Cucullin. When he was angry and gave a stamp with his foot, the whole country shook. Once, by a blow of his fist, he had flattened a thunderbolt till it was flat as a pancake, and ever after he kept it in his pocket to show to anyone who offered to fight with him. Fin was a match for most of the rest of the giants, and had even boasted that the great Cucullin had never—so far—come near him for fear he would get a drubbing. But now, oh grief and sorrow! Cucullin, no less, was on his way, and Fin didn't like the idea—no, not at all!

'How to get round such a terrible fellow, or what to do, I don't know,' went on Fin to his wife in a very doleful tone. 'If I run away while there's still time I shall be a laughing-stock to all the other giants, and a terrible disgrace will be on me. But how to fight with a giant that makes a pancake out of a thunderbolt with one blow of his fist, and that shakes the whole country with one stamp of his foot, I don't know!'

'How far has he got?' asks Oonagh.

'As far as Dungannon,' answers Fin.

'How soon will he be here?' asks she.

'Tomorrow about two o'clock,' answers he, and then he adds with a groan, 'And meet him I shall for my thumb tells me so.'

'Now, now, my dear! Don't fret and don't be cast down!' answers Oonagh. 'Let's see if I can't be the one to bring you out of your great trouble!'

'For the love of all the saints, Oonagh my darling, do what you can! Else for sure I'll either be skinned like a rabbit before your eyes, or else have my name disgraced before the whole tribe of giants. Oh, my grief! Oh, my sorrow! If this isn't just a regular earthquake of a fellow, and him with a pancake in his pocket that was once a thunderbolt!'

'For shame on you, Fin! Be easy now! Pancake, did you say? See now if I can't treat that bully boy to some feeding that'll give him a sore tooth! Leave your moaning and lamenting now, Fin! If I can't get round and circumvent that great lump of a fellow, never trust Oonagh again.'

With that she went to where her skeins of wool were hung out to dry after she had dyed them and she took nine long strands of all the colours she had. She platted the wool-threads three and three, and when it was done she tied one plait round her right arm, one round her right ankle and the third and longest she tied right round her, over her heart.

She'd done all this several times before, when Fin was in trouble, so his mind got a bit firmer when he saw what she was at, for the truth is she hadn't ever failed yet when she had got the threads on her.

'Is there time for me to go round to the neighbours?' Oonagh asked.

'There is time,' said Fin. So off she set and she went to this one and that. When she came back Fin saw that she had borrowed a whole load of griddles —which are thin irons, like huge plates, for making scones or flat bread over a turf fire. Then he saw how she kneaded enough dough to make as many griddle loaves as she had irons. One she cooked in the proper way and made a good round flat loaf of it— big as a cart-wheel nearly—but all the rest were made in a very strange way, for she made them two-sided, each with an iron griddle hidden in the middle. As each one was done, she put it away in the bread-cupboard. Then she made a big milk cheese and she boiled a whole side of bacon, set it to cool, and began to boil a sackful of cabbages.

By this time it was evening, the evening of the day before Cucullin was to come, and the last thing Oonagh did was to light a high smoking bonfire on the hill outside and to put her fingers in her mouth to give three whistles. This was to let Cucullin know that strangers were invited to Knockmany, for that was the way that the Irish, long ago, would be giving a sign to travellers that they could come in. Oonagh didn't tell Fin about her plans that night, but she did ask him a few things about Cucullin, and one of the things that Fin told her was that Cucullin's mighty strength lay in just the one place, and that was the middle finger of his right hand.

Next morning, as you can guess, Fin was on the lookout, and after a while he saw how his enemy Cucullin—as tall as a church tower—was striding along across the valley.

Back into the house went Fin and his face was as white as Oonagh's milk cheese when he was telling her the news. But Oonagh only smiled, she had something ready for Fin too.

'Now Fin dear! Take it more easy! Be guided by me. Here's the cradle that the children are too old for now, and here's a white bonnet, and here's a nightgown of mine that will look for all the world like a baby's robe when you have it on over your shirt. Dress yourself up, lie down snug in the cradle, and cover yourself with the quilt, say nothing, and be guided by me, for this day you must pass for your own child.'

Fin was shaking with fear and he was scarcely tucked up, when there came a regular thunder of a knock on the door.

'Come in and welcome!' cried Oonagh, and, with that, a great huge man twice as big as old Fin, opened the door. And who was it but the mighty Cucullin himself, as punctual to his time as the stars themselves.

'God save all here,' says he in a great rumbling voice. 'And is this where the famous Fin lives?'

'Indeed and it is! Come in and rest, honest man.'

'It's Mrs. Fin you'll be?' says he, coming in and sitting down.

'Indeed and I am, and a fine strong husband I have,' says she.

'Aye,' says he, 'he has the name of being one of the best giants in Ireland, but all the same there's one come that is very willing to try to get the better of him in a fair fight.'

'Dear me!' says Oonagh. 'Isn't that a grievous pity now, for he left the house in a fury this very morning at the first of the light. Word had come that a great big bully of a giant by the name of Cucullin had gone down to look for him on the northern coast of the sea—the place where the Irish giants are building their causeway to get to Scotland. Saints above! But I hope for the poor ignorant fellow's sake that he doesn't find Fin, for Fin'll make paste of Cucullin this day, he's in such a fury!'

'It's I am Cucullin, and it's I am after fighting with Fin!' answered Cucullin, frowning. 'This twelvemonth I'm after looking for him, and it's Fin that will be ground to paste, not me!'

'My sorrow! I'm thinking that you never saw Fin,' said Oonagh, shaking her head.

'How could I see Fin,' answered Cucullin, 'and him dodging all the while to get away from me like as if he was a snipe on a bog?'

'Fin dodging to get away from you, is it, you poor little creature?' says Oonagh, 'I tell you it'll be the black day for you if ever you do see Fin, and let's only hope the wild furious temper that is on him now will have cooled a bit, or else it's rushing to your death you'd be. Rest here a while and when you go it's me that will pray to the holy saints that you never catch up with Fin.'

Cucullin began to wonder a bit about such words, so he didn't speak for a while, and presently Oonagh said, looking about her:

'Isn't that just a terrible wind that's blowing in at the door and making the smoke come down! Fin always helps me when it does that. As he's from home, perhaps you'd be civil enough to do the job for me?'

'What job is that?' asked Cucullin.

'Oh, just to turn the house round for me. That's what Fin always does.'

This made Cucullin wonder a bit more. However, he got up and then Oonagh noticed that, as he stood there, he pulled at the middle finger of his right hand till it gave three little cracks, and she remembered how Fin had told her that it was in this finger that Cucullin's mighty strength lay.

Well, after that he stumped outside on his great legs, put his two great arms round the house and turned it round, just as Oonagh had asked him to do.

Fin, hiding in the cradle, felt ready to die with fear to see the like of that, for of course he never *had* turned the house for Oonagh, no, not in all the long time they'd been married.

But Oonagh, who was outside with Cucullin, gave a sweet smile and a plain 'thank you' making out that turning a whole house round was as easy as opening a door.

'Since you're so civil, perhaps you'd do another obliging thing for me, Fin being away,' says she.

'What obliging thing is that?' asked Cucullin.

'Nothing very great,' says she. 'But after this spell of dry weather, we've been after enduring, I'm having to go down the hill for every drop of water. Only last night Fin promised me he'd get at a spring of water there is under the rocks at the back. But he left home in such a temper, chasing after you to fight you, that he forgot all about it. I'll have a bite of dinner ready for you, if you'll just pull the rocks asunder for me.'

So she brought Cucullin down to see the place, and indeed it was all rock and part of the mountain itself, with only one small crack in it, so that you could scarcely hear the water gurgling underneath.

It was plain from the look on Cucullin's face that he didn't like the job. However, he pulled his finger three times and took another look, then he pulled it three times again, and had another look, and still he didn't like what he saw, for the job was no less than to rend the mountain itself.

However, after he had pulled his finger yet three times more—that was nine times in all—he stepped down. This time he tore a great cleft in the side of the mountain, and it was four hundred feet deep and half a mile long. (It's there to this day—Lumford's Glen they call it.)

'That's very obliging of you I'm sure,' says Oonagh. 'And now away back to the house, for you to get a bite of dinner, for Fin would be blaming me if I let you go without, even if you are enemies, and even if it's only our own humble fare that I can set before you.'

Fin, you remember, was still in the cradle, and hadn't seen what had been going on outside, but all the same he was quaking and shivering to see Cucullin coming back with Oonagh and sitting down at the table.

Oonagh served the giant with two big cans of butter, the whole side of bacon, and she had the whole sack of cabbages ready boiled for him. Last of all she brought out a pile of the big round flat loaves that she had baked the day before.

'Help yourself, and welcome,' says she.

So Cucullin started on the bacon and cabbages and then he picked up one of the big flat loaves and opened his mouth wide to take a huge bite out of it. But he had scarcely bitten into that bread before he let out a terrible yell.

'Blood and fury!' cries he.

'What's the matter?' asks Oonagh.

'Matter enough!' cries he. 'Here's two of my best teeth cracked. What kind of bread is this?'

'Why,' said Oonagh, making out that she was very much surprised, 'that's only Fin's bread! Even his child in the cradle there can eat it!' With that she took the one flat loaf that hadn't got a griddle inside it, and she went across to Fin where he lay in the cradle, and gave him the bread and a hard nudge.

Cucullin watched, and sure enough the thing in the cradle took a huge bite out of the bread and then started munching.

'Here's another loaf for you, Cucullin!' says Oonagh, shaking her head as if she pitied him. 'Maybe this one'll be softer for you.'

But this one had a griddle inside it as well, and when he tried to bite it Cucullin let out a yell that was louder than the first, for he'd bitten harder, not liking the way Oonagh had seemed to pity him.

This yell of Cucullin's was so loud that it frightened Fin into letting out a yell as well.

'There now, you've gone and upset the child!' says Oonagh. 'If you're not able to eat Fin's bread, why can't you say so quietly?'

But Cucullin hadn't got an answer to that, for he

was beginning to feel a bit frightened. What with turning the house, and what with tearing up the mountain, and now what with seeing Fin's child, though it was still in its cradle, munching that terrible bread before his very eyes, he was beginning to think that it really was a good thing he hadn't found Fin at home. Maybe all that Oonagh had been telling him was nothing but the truth!

'And is it special teeth they all have in Fin's family?' asked Cucullin at last, nursing his own jaw. His mouth was too sore for any more bacon and cabbage.

'Would you like to feel for yourself?' answered Oonagh 'I'll get the little fellow to open his mouth for you. But perhaps you'd be afraid of him? It's rather far back in his mouth his teeth are—just put in your longest finger!'

Well, can you guess now what happened? Indeed perhaps you'd hardly believe it, if you didn't know already that there's hardly an end to the foolishness of giants. Yes, that was it!

Cucullin, with a little bit of help from Oonagh, was so foolish as to put in that one special finger of his, the middle finger of his right hand, right into Fin's mouth! Well, maybe Fin wasn't the bravest or the wisest, but all the same he was wise enough to give a good hard bite when he had such a chance as that! So now there stood Cucullin without his finger, and worse than that, without his strength. So at last, Fin plucked up his courage, jumped out of the cradle and then Cucullin thought best to run for it.

Away and away, all down Knockmany Hill Fin chased him, for if Cucullin's strength was gone, he could still run. So at last, since he couldn't catch him, Fin came back, and by then Oonagh had taken the griddles out of the loaves. So the two of them sat down in peace to eat what was left of the dinner that clever Oonagh had set for Cucullin.

4 cups sifted flour
1 teaspoon salt
1 teaspoon sugar
2 teaspoons baking soda
About 1 cup buttermilk

Sift the dry ingredients several times through your fingers. Add the milk gradually, mixing well. The dough should not be too dry. Turn it out onto a floured board and knead lightly a few times. Roll it out to about ¾-inch thick. Cut in pieces any size you want, and cook on a hot greased griddle for about 10 minutes on each side. Serve hot with butter and honey.

*How many loaves of griddle bread can a giant eat on an empty stomach?*

Only one—after that his stomach isn't empty.

# Dwarf Long Nose

In a large town in Germany there lived, some hundred years ago, a cobbler and his wife. They were poor and hard-working. The man sat all day in a little stall at the street corner and mended any shoes that were brought him. His wife sold the fruit and vegetables they grew in their garden and as her goods were always temptingly spread out she had plenty of customers.

The couple had a son called Jem, a handsome, pleasant-faced boy of twelve. He used to sit by his mother in the market and would carry home what people bought from her, for which they often gave him a pretty flower, or a slice of cake, or even some small coin.

One day Jem and his mother sat as usual in the market place with plenty of herbs and vegetables spread out on the board, and in some baskets pears, apples, and apricots. Jem cried his wares at the top of his voice, "This way, gentlemen! See these lovely cabbages and these fresh herbs! Early apples, ladies, early pears and apricots, and all cheap. Come, buy, buy!"

As he cried a ragged old woman came shuffling across the market place. She had a small sharp face, all wrinkled, with red eyes, and a thin hooked nose which nearly met her chin. She leaned on a tall stick and limped and stumbled along as if she were going to fall on her nose at any moment.

When she came to the stall where Jem and his mother were, she stopped.

"Are you Hannah the herb seller?" she asked in a croaky voice as her head shook to and fro.

"Yes, I am," was the answer. "Can I serve you?"

"We'll see, we'll see! Let me look at those herbs. I wonder if you've got what I want," said the old woman as she thrust a pair of hideous hands into the herb basket, and began turning over all the herbs with her skinny fingers, often holding them up to her nose and sniffing at them.

The cobbler's wife felt much disgusted at seeing her wares treated like this, but she dared not speak. When the crone had turned over the whole basket she muttered, "Bad stuff, bad stuff, much better fifty years ago—all bad."

This made Jem very angry.

"You are a rude old woman," he cried out. "First you mess all our nice herbs about with your hideous fingers and sniff at them with your long nose till no one else will care to buy them, and then you say it's all bad stuff, though the duke's cook himself buys all his herbs from us."

The old woman looked sharply at the saucy boy, laughed unpleasantly and said, "So you don't like my long nose? Well, you shall have one yourself, right down to your chin."

As she spoke she shuffled towards the cabbages, took up one after another, squeezed them hard, and threw them back, muttering again, "Bad stuff, bad stuff."

"Don't waggle your head in that horrid way," begged Jem. "Your neck is as thin as a cabbage-stalk, and it might easily break and your head fall into the basket, and then who would buy anything?"

"Don't you like thin necks?" laughed the old woman. "Then you shan't have any, but a head stuck close between your shoulders so that it may be quite sure not to fall off."

"Don't talk such nonsense to the child," Jem's

mother said at last. "If you wish to buy, please make haste, as you are keeping other customers away."

"Very well, I will do as you ask," said the old woman, with an angry look. "I'll buy these six cabbages, but, as you see, I can only walk with my stick and can carry nothing. Let your boy carry them home for me and I'll pay him for his trouble."

Jem didn't like this, for he was afraid of the old woman, but his mother ordered him to go, so he gathered the cabbages into a basket and followed the old woman across the market place.

It took her more than half an hour to get to a distant part of town, but at last she stopped in front of a small tumble-down house. She drew a rusty old hook from her pocket and stuck it into a little hole in the door, which suddenly flew open. How surprised Jem was when they went in! The house was splendidly furnished, the walls and ceiling of marble, the furniture of ebony inlaid with gold and precious stones, the floor of such smooth slippery glass that Jem tumbled down more than once.

The old woman took out a silver whistle and blew it. Immediately a lot of guinea pigs came running down the stairs, but Jem thought it rather odd that they all walked on their hind legs, and wore nut-shells for shoes and men's clothes.

"Where are my slippers, lazy crew?" cried the crone, and hit about with her stick. "How long am I to stand here waiting?"

They rushed upstairs again and returned with a pair of coconuts lined with leather, which she put on her feet. Now all limping and shuffling was at an end. She threw away her stick and walked briskly across the glass floor, drawing Jem after her. At last she paused in a room which looked almost like a kitchen, it was so full of pots and pans, but the tables were of mahogany and the sofas and chairs covered with the richest fabrics.

"Sit down," said the old woman pleasantly, and she pushed Jem into a corner of a sofa and put a table in front of him. "You've had a long walk and a heavy load to carry, and I must give you something for your trouble. Wait a bit, and I'll give you some nice soup you'll remember as long as you live."

So saying, she whistled again. First came in the guinea pigs in men's clothing. They had tied on large kitchen aprons, and in their belts were stuck carving knives and sauce ladles and such things. After them came a number of squirrels. They too walked on their hind legs, wore full Turkish trousers, and little green velvet caps on their heads. They seemed to be scullions, for they clambered up the walls and brought down pots and pans, eggs, flour, butter, and herbs, which they carried to the stove. Here the old woman was bustling about, and Jem could see that she was cooking something special for him. At last the broth began to bubble and boil, and she drew off the saucepan and poured its contents into a silver bowl, which she set before Jem.

"There, my boy, eat this soup and then you'll have everything which pleased you so much about me. And you shall be a clever cook too, but the real herb—no, the *real* herb you'll never find. Why didn't your mother have it in her basket?"

Jem didn't understand what she was talking about, but he found the soup delicious. His mother had often given him nice things, but nothing had ever seemed so good as this. The smell of the herbs and spices rose from the bowl, and the soup tasted both sweet and sharp at the same time, and was very strong. As he was finishing it the guinea pigs lit some Arabian incense, which gradually filled the room with clouds of blue vapor. They grew thicker and thicker and the scent nearly overpowered the boy. He reminded himself that he must get back to his mother, but whenever he tried to rouse himself to go he sank back again drowsily, and at last he fell sound asleep in the corner of the sofa.

Strange dreams came to him. He thought the old woman wrapped him up in a squirrel skin, and that he went about with the other squirrels and guinea pigs, and waited on her. First he learned to clean her coconut shoes with oil and to rub them up. Then he learned to catch the little sun moths and rub them through the finest sieves, and the flour from them he made into soft bread for the toothless old woman.

In this way he passed from one kind of service to another, spending a year in each, till in the fourth year he was promoted to the kitchen. Here he worked his way up from kitchen boy to head pastry cook, and reached the greatest perfection. He could make all the most difficult dishes, and two hundred different kinds of patties, soup flavored with every sort of herb—he had learned it all, and learned it well.

Seven years passed. One day, as the old woman was going out, she ordered Jem to kill and pluck a chicken, stuff it with herbs, and have it very nicely roasted by the time she got back. Jem killed and plucked the chicken and then went to fetch the herbs to stuff it with. In the storeroom he noticed a half-opened cupboard that he had not seen before. Inside were a lot of baskets from which came a strong and pleasant smell. He opened one and found a very uncommon herb in it. The stems and leaves were a bluish green, and above them was a little flower of a deep bright red, edged with yellow. He gazed at the flower, smelled it, and found it gave the same strong strange perfume which came from the soup the old woman had made him. But the smell was so sharp that he began to sneeze again and again, and at last—he woke up!

There he lay on the old woman's sofa and stared about him in surprise. "Well, what odd dreams one does have, to be sure!" he said to himself. "Why, I could have sworn I had been a squirrel, a companion of guinea pigs and such creatures, and had become a great cook, too. How Mother will laugh when I tell her! But won't she scold me, though, for sleeping away here in a strange house, instead of helping her at market!"

He jumped up and prepared to go. All his limbs seemed stiff from his long sleep, especially his neck, for he could not move his head easily. He laughed about being still so drowsy that he kept knocking his nose against the wall or cupboards. The squirrels and guinea pigs ran whimpering after him, as though they would like to go too, and he begged them to come when he reached the door, but they all turned and ran quickly back into the house again.

This part of the town was unknown to Jem. He was puzzled by the narrow winding streets and by the crowd of people, who seemed excited about some show. From what he heard, he fancied they were going to see a dwarf, for he heard them call out: "Just look at the ugly dwarf!" "What a long nose he has, and see how his head is stuck in between his shoulders, and only look at his ugly hands!" If he had not been in such a hurry to get back to his mother, he would have gone too, for he loved shows with giants and dwarfs and the like.

When he reached the market place there sat his mother, with a good deal of fruit still in her baskets, so he felt he could not have slept so very long. It struck him that she was sad, for she did not call to the passersby, but sat with her head resting on her hand, and as he came nearer he saw she looked pale.

He hesitated, not knowing what to do. At last he slipped behind her, laid a hand on her arm, and said, "Mother, what is the matter? Are you angry with me?"

She turned round quickly and jumped up with a cry of horror.

"What do you want, you hideous dwarf?" she cried. "Get away; I can't bear such tricks."

"But, Mother, what's the matter with you?" repeated Jem, quite frightened. "You can't be well. Why do you want to drive your son away?"

"I have said already, get away," replied Hannah, quite angrily. "You won't get anything out of me by your games, you monstrosity."

"She must be wandering in her mind," murmured the lad to himself. "How can I manage to get her home? Dearest Mother, do look at me close. Can't you see I am your own son Jem?"

"Well, did you ever hear such impudence?" asked Hannah, turning to a neighbor. "Just see that frightful dwarf—would you believe that he wants me to think he is my son Jem?"

Then all the market women came round and scolded Jem as hard as they could for making game of Mrs. Hannah, who had never got over the loss of her son, stolen from her seven years ago.

Poor Jem did not know what to make of it all. He was sure he had gone to market with his mother only that morning, had helped to set out the stall, had gone to the old woman's house, where he had some soup and a little nap, and now, when he came back, they were all talking of seven years. And they called him an ugly dwarf! Why, what had happened to him? When he found that his mother would really have nothing to do with him he turned away with tears in his eyes, and went sadly down the street towards his father's stall.

"Now I'll see whether he will know me," thought Jem. "I'll stand by the door and talk to him."

The cobbler was so busy working that he did not see Jem for some time. When he happened to look up he let shoes, thread, and everything fall to the ground, and cried out, "Good heavens! what is that?"

"Good evening, master," said the boy, as he stepped inside. "How do you do?"

"Very ill, little sir," replied the father, to Jem's surprise, for he did not seem to know him. "Business does not go well. I am all alone, and am getting old, and an apprentice is costly."

"But haven't you a son who could learn your trade?"

"I had one, called Jem. He would have been a tall sturdy lad of twenty by this time, and able to help me well. Why, when he was only twelve he was quite sharp and quick, and had learned many things. He was a good-looking boy too, and so pleasant that customers were taken by him. Well, well! so goes the world!"

"But where is your son?" asked Jem.

"Heaven only knows!" replied the cobbler. "Seven

years ago he was stolen from us in the market place."

"*Seven years ago!*" exclaimed Jem.

"Yes, though it seems but yesterday that my wife came home crying, and saying the child had not come back all day. I always thought and said that something of the kind would happen. Jem was a handsome boy, and everyone made much of him. My wife was so proud of him and liked him to carry the vegetables and things to grand folks' houses where he was made much of. But I used to say, "Take care—the town is large, there are plenty of bad people in it—keep a sharp eye on Jem." And so it happened. For one day an old woman came and bought a lot of things—more than she could carry. So my wife, being a kindly soul, lent her the boy, and—we have never seen him since."

"And that was seven years ago, you say?"

"Yes, seven years. We searched everywhere, but it was all in vain. No one seemed to know the old woman who bought the vegetables; only one old woman, who is ninety years old, said it might have been the witch Herbaline, who came into town once in every fifty years to buy things."

As his father spoke, things grew clearer in Jem's mind. He saw now that he had not been dreaming, but had really served the witch seven years in the shape of a squirrel. As he thought it over rage filled his heart. Seven years of his youth had been stolen from him, and what had he got in return? To learn to rub up coconuts, to polish glass floors, and to be taught cooking by guinea pigs! He stood there thinking, till at last his father asked him, "Is there anything I can do for you, young sir? Shall I make you a pair of slippers, or perhaps"—with a smile—"a case for your nose?"

"Why should I want a case for my nose?" asked Jem.

"Well, everyone to his taste," replied the cobbler, "but I must say if I had such a nose I would have a nice red leather cover made for it. Here is a nice piece. Think what a protection it would be to you. As it is, you must be constantly knocking up against things."

The lad was dumb with fright. He felt his nose. It was thick, and quite two hands long. So, then the witch had changed his shape, and that was why his own mother did not know him, and called him an ugly dwarf!

"Master," said he, "have you got a glass that I could see myself in?"

"Young sir, there is no need to waste your time looking in a glass. Besides, I have none here, but if you must have one you had better ask Urban the barber, who lives over the way, to lend you his. Good morning."

So saying, he gently pushed Jem into the street, shut the door, and went back to his work.

Jem stepped across to the barber's shop.

"Good morning, Urban," said he. "May I look at myself in your glass for a moment?"

"With pleasure," said the barber, laughing, and all the people in his shop fell to laughing also. "You are a pretty youth, with your swan-like neck, smooth hands and small nose. No wonder you are rather vain. But look as long as you like at yourself."

So spoke the barber, and a titter ran round the room. Meantime Jem had stepped up to the mirror, and stood gazing sadly at his reflection. Tears came to his eyes.

"No wonder you did not know your child again, dear mother," he thought. "He wasn't like this when you were so proud of his looks."

His eyes had grown quite small, like pigs' eyes, his nose was huge and hung down over his mouth and chin, his neck seemed to have disappeared altogether, and his head was fixed stiffly between his shoulders. He was no taller than he had been seven years ago, when he was twelve years old, but he made

up for it in breadth. His back and chest had grown
into lumps like two great sacks. His legs were small
and spindly, but his arms were as large as those of a
well-grown man, with gnarled hands, and long
skinny fingers.

Then he remembered the morning when he had
first seen the old woman, and her threats to him, and
without saying a word he left the barber's shop.

He returned to the market place and begged his
mother to listen quietly to him. He reminded her of
the day when he went away with the old woman,
and of many things in his childhood, and told her
how he had been bewitched for seven years. Hannah
did not know what to think—the story was so strange.
It seemed impossible to think her handsome son
and this hideous dwarf were the same. At last she
decided to talk to her husband about it. She gathered
up her baskets, told Jem to follow her, and went
straight to the cobbler's stall.

"Look here," she said, "this creature says he is our
lost son. He has been telling me how he was stolen
seven years ago, and bewitched by an old woman."

"Indeed!" interrupted the cobbler angrily. "Did
he tell you this? Wait a minute, you rascal! Why I
told him all about it myself only an hour ago, and
then he goes off to humbug you. So you were be-

witched, my son, were you? Wait a bit, and I'll bewitch you!"

So saying, he caught up a bundle of straps, and hit out at Jem so hard that he ran off crying.

The poor little dwarf roamed about all the rest of the day without food or drink, and at night was glad to lie down and sleep on the steps of a church. He woke next morning with the first rays of light, and began to think what he could do to earn a living. Suddenly he remembered that he was an excellent cook, and he determined to look out for a place.

He decided to go to the palace, for he knew that the duke who reigned over the country was fond of good things.

When he reached the palace all the servants crowded about him, and made fun of him. At last their shouts and laughter grew so loud that the head steward rushed out, crying, "For goodness sake, be quiet, can't you? Don't you know his highness is still asleep?"

Some of the servants ran off at once, and others pointed out Jem. Indeed, the steward found it hard to keep himself from laughing at the comic sight, but he ordered the servants off and led the dwarf into his own room.

When he heard him ask for a place as cook he

said, "You make some mistake, my lad. I think you want to be the duke's dwarf, don't you?"

"No, sir, I am an experienced cook, and if you will kindly take me to the head cook he may find me of some use."

"Well, as you will. But believe me, you would have an easier place as the ducal dwarf."

So saying, the steward led him to the head cook's room. "Sir," asked Jem, bowing so low his nose nearly touched the floor, "do you want an experienced cook?"

The head cook looked him over from head to foot, and burst out laughing.

"You a cook! Do you suppose our cooking stoves are so low that you can look into any saucepan on them? Oh, my dear little fellow, whoever sent you to me wanted to make fun of you."

But the dwarf was not to be put off by the head cook.

"What matters an extra egg or two, or a little butter or flour and spice more or less, in such a house as this?" said he. "Name any dish you wish to have cooked, and give me the materials I ask for, and you shall see."

He said much more, and at last persuaded the head cook to give him a trial.

They went into the kitchen—a huge place with at

least twenty fireplaces, always alight. A little stream of clear water ran through the room, and live fish were kept at one end of it. Everything in the kitchen was of the best, and swarms of cooks and scullions were busy preparing dishes.

When the head cook came in with Jem everyone stood quite still.

"What has his highness ordered for luncheon?" asked the head cook.

"Sir, his highness has graciously ordered a Danish soup and red Hamburg dumplings."

"Good," said the head cook. "Have you heard, and do you feel equal to making these dishes? Not that you will be able to make the dumplings, for they are a secret recipe."

"Is that all!" said Jem, who had often made both dishes. "Nothing easier. Let me have some eggs, a piece of wild boar, and such and such roots and herbs for the soup. As for the dumplings," he added in a low voice to the head cook, "I shall want four different kinds of meat, some wine, a duck's marrow, some ginger, and a herb called heal-well."

"Why," cried the astonished cook, "where did you learn cooking? Yes, those are the exact ingredients, but we never used the herb heal-well, which, I am sure, must be an improvement."

And now Jem was allowed to try his hand. He

could barely reach up to the stove, but by putting a wide plank on two chairs he managed very well. All the cooks stood round to look on, and could not help admiring the quick, clever way in which he set to work. At last, when all was ready, Jem ordered the two dishes to be put on the fire till he gave the word. Then he began to count, "One, two, three," till he got to five hundred when he cried, "Now!" The saucepans were taken off, and he invited the head cook to taste.

The head cook solemnly approached, tasted the dishes, and smacked his lips over them. "First rate, indeed!" he exclaimed. "You certainly are a master of the art, little fellow, and the herb heal-well gives a particular relish."

As he was speaking, the duke's valet came to say that his highness was ready for luncheon, so it was served at once. The head cook took Jem to his own room, but hardly had time to question him before he was ordered to go to the duke.

The duke was looking much pleased. He had emptied the dishes, and was wiping his mouth as the head cook came in. "Who cooked my luncheon today?" asked he. "Your dumplings are always good, but I don't think I ever tasted anything so delicious as they were to-day. Who made them?"

"It is a strange story, your highness," said the cook, and told him the whole matter, which surprised the duke so much that he sent for the dwarf and asked him many questions. Of course, Jem could not say he had been turned into a squirrel, but he said he was without parents and had been taught cooking by an old woman.

"If you stay with me," said the duke, "you shall have fifty ducats a year, besides a new coat and a couple of pairs of trousers. You shall be called assistant head cook, and cook my luncheon yourself, and direct what I shall have for dinner."

Jem bowed low, and promised to obey his new master in all things.

He lost no time in setting to work, and everyone rejoiced at having him in the kitchen, for the duke was not a patient man, and had been known to throw plates and dishes at his cooks and servants if the things served were not quite to his taste. Now all was changed. He never even grumbled at anything, had five meals instead of three, thought everything delicious, and grew fatter daily.

And so Jem lived on for two years, much respected, and only saddened when he thought of his parents. One day passed much like another till the following incident happened.

Dwarf Long Nose—as he was always called—made a practice of doing his marketing as much as possible himself, and whenever time allowed went to the market to buy his poultry and fruit. One morning he was in the goose market, looking for some nice fat geese. No one thought of laughing at his appearance now. He was known as the duke's special cook, and every goose-woman felt honored if his nose turned her way.

Noticing one woman sitting apart with a number of geese, he went up to her, felt and weighed her geese, and, finding them very good, bought three and the cage to put them in, hoisted them on his broad shoulders, and set off on his way back.

As he went, it struck him that two of the geese were honking and hissing as geese do, but the third sat quite still, only heaving a deep sigh now and then, like a human being. "That goose is ill," thought he. "I must kill and dress her quickly."

But the goose answered him quite distinctly:

> "Squeeze too tight
> And I'll bite,
> If my neck a twist you gave
> I'd bring you to an early grave."

Startled, the dwarf set down the cage, and the goose gazed at him with sad, wise eyes and sighed again.

"Good gracious!" said Long Nose. "So you can speak, Mistress Goose. I never should have thought it! Well, don't be anxious. I know better than to hurt so rare a bird. But I bet you were not always in this plumage—wasn't I a squirrel myself for a time?"

"You are right," said the goose. "I was not born in this wretched shape. Ah! no one ever thought that Mimi, the daughter of the great Weatherbold, would be killed for the ducal table."

"Be quite easy, Mistress Mimi," comforted Jem. "As sure as I'm an honest man and assistant head cook to his highness, no one shall harm you. I will make a hutch for you in my own rooms, and you shall be well fed, and I'll come and talk to you as much as I can. I'll tell all the other cooks that I am fattening up a goose on very special food for the duke, and at the first good opportunity I'll set you free."

The goose thanked him with tears in her eyes, and the dwarf kept his word. He killed the other two geese for dinner, but built a little shed for Mimi in one of his rooms, under the pretense of fattening her under his own eye. He spent all his spare time talking to her and comforting her, and fed her on all the daintiest dishes. They confided their histories to each other, and Jem learned that the goose was the daughter of the wizard Weatherbold, who lived on the island of Gothland. He fell out with another wizard who got the better of him by cunning and treachery, and to revenge himself turned his daughter into a goose and carried her off to this distant place. When Long Nose told her his story she said, "I know a little of these matters, and what you say shows me that you are under a herb enchantment— that is to say, that if you can find the herb whose smell woke you up the spell would be broken."

This was but small comfort for Jem, for how and where was he to find the herb?

About this time the duke had a visit from a neighboring prince, a friend of his. He sent for Long Nose and said to him, "Now is the time to show what you can really do. The prince has better dinners than any one except myself, and is a great judge of cooking. As long as he is here you must take care that my table is served in a manner to surprise him constantly. At the same time, on pain of my displeasure, take care that no dish appears twice. Get everything you wish and spare nothing. I would rather be a poor man than have to blush before him."

The dwarf bowed and answered, "Your highness shall be obeyed. I will do all in my power to please you and the prince."

From this time the little cook was hardly seen except in the kitchen, where, surrounded by his helpers, he gave orders, baked, stewed, flavored and dished up all manner of dishes.

The prince had been a fortnight with the duke, and enjoyed himself mightily. They ate five times a day, and the duke had every reason to be content with the dwarf's talents, for he saw how pleased his guest looked. On the fifteenth day of the visit the duke sent for the dwarf and presented him to the prince.

"You are a wonderful cook," said the prince. "All the time I have been here you have never repeated a dish, and all were excellent. But tell me why you have never served the queen of all dishes, a Suzeraine Pasty?"

The dwarf felt frightened, for he had never heard of this queen of pasties before. But he did not lose his wits and replied:

"I have waited, hoping that your highness' visit here would last some time, for I proposed to celebrate the last day of your stay with this truly royal dish."

"Indeed," laughed the grand duke, "then I suppose you would have waited for the day of my death to treat me to it, for you have never sent it up to me yet. However, you will have to invent some other farewell dish, for the pasty must be on my table tomorrow."

"As your highness pleases," said the dwarf, and took leave.

But it did not please *him* at all. The moment of disgrace seemed at hand, for he had no idea how to make this pasty. He went to his room very sad. As he sat there lost in thought the goose Mimi, who was left free to walk about, came up and asked what was the matter. When she heard she said, "Cheer up, my friend. I know the dish quite well. We often had it at home, and I can guess pretty well how it was made." Then she told him what to put in, adding, "I think that will be all right, and if some trifle is left out perhaps they won't notice."

Sure enough, next day a magnificent pasty all wreathed round with flowers was placed on the table. Jem himself put on his best clothes and went into the dining hall. As he entered the head carver was in the act of cutting up the pie and helping the duke and his guests. The duke took a large mouthful and rolled his eyes as he swallowed it.

"Oh! oh! this may well be called the queen of pasties, and at the same time my dwarf must be called the king of cooks. Don't you think so, dear friend?"

The prince took several small pieces, tasted and examined carefully, and then said with a mysterious and sarcastic smile, "The dish is very nicely made, but the Suzeraine is not quite complete—as I expected."

The duke flew into a rage.

"Dog of a cook," he shouted. "How dare you serve me so? I've a good mind to chop off your head as a punishment."

"For mercy's sake, don't, your highness! I made the pasty according to the best rules. Nothing has been left out. Ask the prince what else I should have put in."

The prince laughed. "I was sure you could not make this dish as well as my cook, friend Long Nose. Know, then, that a herb is wanting called Relish, which is not known in this country, but which gives the pasty its peculiar flavor, and without which your master will never taste it to perfection."

The duke was more furious than ever.

"But I *will* taste it to perfection," he roared. "Either the pasty must be made properly tomorrow or this rascal's head shall come off. Go, scoundrel, I give you twenty-four hours' respite."

The poor dwarf hurried back to his room, and poured out his grief to the goose.

"Oh, is that all," said she, "then I can help you, for my father taught me to know all plants and herbs. Luckily there is a new moon just now, for the herb only springs up at such times. But tell me, are there chestnut trees near the palace?"

"Oh, yes!" Long Nose replied, "near the lake—
only a couple of hundred yards from the palace—is
a large clump of them. But why do you ask?"

"Because the herb only grows near the roots of
chestnut trees," replied Mimi, "so let us lose no time
in finding it. Take me under your arm and put me
down out of doors, and I'll hunt for it."

He did as she bade, and as soon as they were in
the garden put her on the ground. Then she wad-
dled off as fast as she could towards the lake, Jem
hurrying after her with an anxious heart, for he
knew that his life depended on her success. The
goose hunted everywhere, but in vain. She searched
under each chestnut tree, turning every blade of
grass with her bill—nothing to be seen and evening
was drawing on!

Suddenly the dwarf noticed a big old tree standing
alone on the other side of the lake. "Look," he
called out, "let's try our luck there." The goose
fluttered and skipped in front, and he ran after as
fast as his little legs could carry him. The tree cast
a wide shadow, and it was almost dark beneath it,
but suddenly the goose stood still, flapped her wings,
and plucked something, which she held out to her
astonished friend, saying, "There it is, and more
growing here, so you will have all you need."

The dwarf stood gazing at the plant. It gave out a strong sweet scent, which reminded him of the day of his enchantment. The stems and leaves were a bluish green, and it bore a dark, bright red flower with a yellow edge.

"What a wonder!" cried Long Nose. "I do believe this is the very herb which changed me from a squirrel into my present miserable form. Shall I try an experiment?"

"Not yet," said the goose. "Take a handful of the herb with you, and let us go to your rooms. We will collect all your money and clothes together, and then we will test the powers of the herb."

So they went back to Jem's rooms, and here he gathered together some fifty ducats he had saved, his clothes and shoes, and tied them all up in a bundle. Then he plunged his face into the bunch of herbs, and drew in their perfume.

As he did so, all his limbs began to crack and stretch; he felt his head rising about his shoulders. He glanced down at his nose, and saw it grow smaller and smaller. His chest and back grew flat, and his legs grew long.

The goose looked on in amazement. "How tall and handsome you are!" she cried.

Jem was overjoyed, but his happiness did not make him forget all he owed to his friend Mimi.

"I owe you my life and my release," he said, "for without you I should never have regained my natural shape, and would soon have been beheaded. I will take you back to your father, who will certainly know how to disenchant you."

The goose accepted his offer with joy, and they managed to slip out of the palace unnoticed by anyone.

They got through the journey without accident, and the wizard soon released his daughter, and loaded Jem with thanks and valuable presents. Jem hastened back to his native town where his parents readily recognized the handsome young man as their long-lost son. With the money given him by the wizard he opened a shop, which prospered well, and he lived long and happily.

I must not forget to mention that much disturbance was caused in the palace by Jem's sudden disappearance, for when the duke sent orders next day to behead the dwarf, if he had not found the herb, the dwarf was not to be found. The prince hinted that the duke had allowed his cook to escape, and had therefore broken his word. The matter ended in a great war between the two princes, which was known in history as the "Herb War." After many battles a peace was concluded, and this peace became known as the "Pasty Peace," because at the banquet given in its honor the prince's cook dished up the queen of pasties—the Suzeraine—and the duke declared it to be quite excellent.

\*　　\*　　\*

*I have eyes but cannot see;*
*A skin but not a face;*
*When farmers dig up ground for me*
*They find my hiding place.*

A potato

# CHOCOLATE POTATO CAKE

1 cup (2 sticks) butter at room temperature
2 cups sugar
4 eggs
3 ounces (3 squares) unsweetened chocolate, melted
1 cup cold mashed potatoes
1 cup sour milk
2 cups sifted flour
1 teaspoon baking powder
½ teaspoon baking soda
¼ teaspoon salt
1 teaspoon cinnamon
¼ teaspoon nutmeg

Cream the butter and add the sugar gradually. Beat in eggs one at a time. Add the chocolate, potatoes and sour milk.

Sift the dry ingredients together and add to the first mixture. Pour into two greased 9-inch layer cake pans lined with waxed paper, and bake in a 350° F. oven for 35 minutes, or until done. Cool in pans for 10 minutes, then turn out on racks. When cool fill and frost with chocolate butter icing.

¼ cup (½ stick) butter at room temperature
2 ounces (2 squares) unsweetened chocolate, melted
3 cups confectioners' sugar
Hot water—about ¼ cup
Teaspoon vanilla

Combine butter and chocolate. Gradually add confectioners' sugar and enough water to make a smooth consistency. Beat vigorously. Add 1 teaspoon vanilla.

*Cushy cow, bonny, let down thy milk,*
*And I will give thee a gown of silk;*
*A gown of silk and a silver tee,*
*If thou wilt let down thy milk to me.*

*This old charm was used by milkmaids and country*
*women to induce bewitched cows to give their milk.*
*A cushy cow is a hornless cow. The tee is a cowtie.*

## ⤐| MOLASSES MILK SHAKE

1 glass milk, ice cold
2 tablespoons molasses

Blend or shake together

# Pinto Smalto

**T**here once lived a rich merchant who had an only daughter whom he greatly wished to see married, but whenever he spoke of it he found her thoughts a thousand miles away. This made her father the saddest man in the world.

One day when he had to go to the fair he asked Betta (for that was his daughter's name) what she would like him to bring her on his return.

"Father," she answered, "if you love me, bring me fifty pounds of sugar and fifty pounds of sweet almonds with four or six bottles of scented water. And also bring me forty pearls, two sapphires, a few garnets and rubies, with a little spun gold, and above all a kneading trough and a silver grater."

Her father was surprised by her extravagant request but he was unwilling to contradict his daughter. So he went to the fair and on his return brought all she had asked for. As soon as she received these things Betta shut herself up in her room and began to knead a great quantity of almond paste mixed with rose water and perfume. And when it was ready she shaped a handsome youth with hair of spun gold, eyes of sapphires, teeth of pearls, and lips of rubies. And she shaped him with so much grace that he needed only the gift of speech to be perfect.

Now Betta, having heard it said that in answer to the prayers of a certain king of Cyprus a statue had come to life, prayed to the goddess of love. And her prayers were so heartfelt that at last the statue began to open its eyes. At this she prayed still harder and soon the handsome figure began to breathe and to speak, and finally, to walk.

With great joy Betta embraced the youth and taking him by the hand she led him before her father and said, "My dear father, you have always told me that you wished to see me married, and in order to please you I have shaped a bridegroom after my heart's desire."

When the father saw the handsome youth come out of his daughter's room, which he certainly had not entered, he marveled. And admiring his beauty and grace he consented to the marriage at once.

Among the guests at the wedding feast was a great queen in disguise. When she beheld the matchless beauty of Pinto Smalto (for that was the name Betta had given the youth) she desired him for herself.

Now Pinto Smalto had opened his eyes to the world only three hours before and he knew nothing of its trickery. When it was time for the guests to leave he accompanied each to the foot of the stairs as his bride had instructed him. But when he escorted this wicked queen she took him by the hand and led him to her carriage which was waiting in the courtyard and ordered the coachman to drive off to her own country. And there Pinto Smalto, not understanding what had happened to him, became her husband.

When Pinto Smalto did not return from the courtyard Betta went to look for him. Not finding him anywhere she surmised that someone had stolen him because of his great beauty. And when time passed and no one could give her any news of her handsome husband, she disguised herself as a beggar girl and set out in search of him.

She traveled for several months until she came to the house of a kindly old woman who, on hearing of Betta's misfortune, taught her three sayings. The first was: "In the house it rains." The second: "The fountain flows." And the third: "Backsides and drums, fritters and beans, and caraway seed." She told Betta to repeat these words if ever she were in need, and they would help her. Betta wondered at such silly talk but said to herself, "Who knows what good fortune these words may bring?" And she thanked the old woman and went on her way.

After a long journey she came to a beautiful city

called Monterotondo and made her way to the royal palace where she begged for shelter. She was given a small room and while she was resting there she saw Pinto Smalto pass by. She was so overcome with joy that she was about to speak to him, but remembering her wretched appearance she decided instead to try out the first saying the old woman had taught her. No sooner had she uttered the words, "In the house it rains," when there appeared before her a beautiful little cart of gold set with jewels that was able to move around the room by itself. It was a marvelous sight, and when the young ladies of the court saw it they hastened to tell the queen. The queen came at once and when she saw the magnificent little cart she asked Betta to sell it to her. Betta replied, "Although I am poor I will not sell it for all the gold in the world. But if you will let me spend one night in your husband's company I will give you the cart."

The queen was astonished that the beggar girl would refuse so much wealth for a mere whim but she was more than willing to grant her wish. However, when night came, the queen gave Pinto Smalto a sleeping potion and he soon fell fast asleep. In vain Betta tried to wake him, and when she could not she began to weep and reproach him. In the

morning the queen came and said to Betta, "Now be content."

But Betta's longing for Pinto Smalto to recognize her was so great she spoke the second words, "The fountains flows," and there appeared a golden cage with a beautiful bird inside made of gold and precious stones and singing like a nightingale.

When the queen saw the beautiful bird she wanted it and asked Betta to sell it to her. But Betta answered as before, "Although I am poor I will not sell it for all the gold in the world. But if you will let me spend the night in your husband's company I will give the bird to you."

The queen thought Betta very foolish but agreed to her request. However, when night came, she again gave Pinto Smalto a sleeping potion and when Betta came to his room Pinto Smalto was fast asleep. Betta's tears and reproaches would have moved a stone to compassion, but Pinto Smalto slept so soundly he did not hear a word.

As soon as it was day the queen came for the bird and left the unhappy Betta wringing her hands at the trick that had been played on her twice.

That morning Pinto Smalto went to gather figs in a garden outside the city gate. On the way he met a cobbler whose room at the palace was next to Bet-

ta's, and who had heard her weeping for her beloved lost husband. He told Pinto Smalto all that Betta had said. The king, who was beginning to grow wise, suspected how matters stood and resolved to stay awake that night.

Betta determined to make a third try so she said the words, "Backsides and drums, fritters and beans, and caraway seed," and instantly there appeared bolts of fine linen embroidered with gold and silver thread. When the queen saw the rich fabrics she bargained for them as before. And Betta replied, "Although I am poor I will not sell them for all the gold in the world. But if you will let me spend the night in your husband's company I will give them to you."

Then the queen thought to herself, "What can I lose by indulging this foolish girl's whim?" So she accepted the beautiful gifts. And when night came she gave Pinto Smalto the sleeping potion. But this time Pinto Smalto only pretended to drink the potion and spat it out as soon as he was alone.

That night Betta repeated her story, telling Pinto Smalto how she had kneaded him with her own hands out of sugar and almonds, made his hair of spun gold and his eyes and mouth of precious stones, and how life had been given him by the goddess of love in answer to Betta's prayers. She told him how he had been stolen from her and how she had searched the world to find him.

When Pinto Smalto, who was only pretending to be asleep, heard these words he remembered as in a dream all that had happened to him. And he embraced Betta and comforted her. Then, entering the chamber of the sleeping queen, Pinto Smalto took all the beautiful things that the queen had taken from Betta and he and Betta set off together for her father's house. His joy and happiness on seeing his daughter again was so great that he became as carefree as a young man, and together they all lived happily ever after.

As for the queen, finding neither her husband nor the beggar girl nor the jewels, she pulled her hair in desperation. But let no one forget that it is said: "He who deceives must not complain if he is deceived."

*Crusaders of the Middle Ages brought this confection to Italy from the Middle East. It is usually shaped into miniature fruits, vegetables, flowers or animals, but human figures are fun to make too.*

1 cup almond paste (8-ounce can)
1 egg white
1½ cups sifted confectioners' sugar
Few drops of rose water (sold in drugstores)

Mash paste until slightly softened. Beat egg white until fluffy and blend into paste. Add sugar and rose water and mix until smooth enough to handle, adding more sugar if mixture is too sticky, or rose water if it crumbles. Knead until smooth. Chill in refrigerator for a few hours before shaping into your heart's desire.

If you have a talent for sculpture you can use it here. Otherwise roll marzipan to ¼-inch thickness between two sheets of waxed paper. Remove top paper and cut out desired shapes. Dry on rack overnight.

Marzipan can be painted with food coloring diluted with water or it can be brushed with egg yolk and baked in a preheated 450° F. oven until golden brown on top (about 10 minutes). Decorate your shapes with raisins or currants for eyes, pieces of candied cherry for the mouth, shredded coconut for the hair, etc. by placing these pieces on the unbaked marzipan or by dipping them into egg white and arranging them on the baked marzipan while it is still warm.

1 medium-sized potato
1 pound confectioners' sugar
1 cup shredded coconut
1 teaspoon vanilla
1 ounce (1 square) unsweetened chocolate

Boil and mash the potato. Add confectioners' sugar gradually, then the coconut and vanilla. Mix well.

Drop by teaspoonfuls onto wax paper, twirling into a peak, or press into a buttered pan and cut in squares.

Melt the chocolate over hot water and pour over the top of the candy.

\* \* \*

*Hard as a rock, not rock;*
*White as milk, not milk;*
*Sweet as sugar, not sugar.*

A coconut

# The Miller, His Cook
# and the King

Once upon a time there lived a miller who was so prosperous that he even ordered a first-rate chef from town to come and cook for him. His mills ran night and day: it was a joy to watch the great wheels spin in the river. The miller himself rarely bothered about them, for he had well-paid help to keep them running. If he happened by, it was only because he wanted an airing. He liked to go for long walks and intended to take them oftener than he did, in the hope of exercising away some of the enormous belly he had grown from years of easy living.

He had not always been so carefree. As a penniless young miller he had labored from dawn to dark, even on through the night, in a small rickety mill with only one wheel. But once fortune began to smile on him she kept on smiling, for he was thrifty, circumspect, and honorable—a man who never missed an opportunity for honest earnings. After the first year at the old mill there was an abundance of work and money. Moreover, he had saved enough to set another wheel turning beside the first, grinding out a double quantity of golden wheat and bringing him a doubled amount of bright coins. The third year three wheels turned and three stones crunched in a mill so handsomely improved that people called it the finest in the whole region.

There was more than enough work, and food aplenty. Each year the miller counted up a goodly sum and, instead of stashing it away in a stocking, he put it to good use, building one new mill after another along the rushing stream. It became a special pleasure to hear the sounds of the wheels' turning and splashing which filled the air.

Since he had enough men to do the milling, our miller began to take extra time for himself to live a more leisurely existence, "to try the life of great lords," he would jokingly say. And why not, indeed, when there was as much money around the house as drops in a summer shower?

It was in order to enjoy his wealth in a lordly manner that the miller hired an excellent cook, who prepared such mouth-watering food that the miller lived every day in anticipation of the next meal. The cook was also a great joker, and in his company the miller enjoyed many a mirthful hour.

Then one day he felt the consequences of his cook's waggish humor. In an idle moment the cook took up a paintbrush and wrote over the house in big letters:

"I LIVE WITHOUT A CARE IN THE WORLD."

That was an open invitation to trouble, and trouble came riding by only a few days later in the person of the king himself. His reaction after reading the odd inscription was to declare, "What's the meaning of this? Everyone the world over has cares! If the man of the house lives so thoughtless a life, I'll give him something to think about!"

And the king dispatched his minister to the miller with the following command. In a month's time he was to appear at court with answers to these questions: How many stars shine in the sky? How far is it from the earth to the heavens? What is the king worth? What is the king thinking? If the miller failed to come at the appointed time, or did not have satisfactory answers to the questions, he would lose his head.

This was no joke the miller could laugh his way

out of. What a calamity it would be to lose his head at a time when he had everything except bird's milk and frog's feathers!

Concentrate as he would, no answers came to him. He lost his appetite and could not even enjoy a glass of golden wine. He was so worried that his stomach shrank noticeably, and people seeing him grow thinner day by day shook their heads and whispered, "It's the Judgment Day approaching, for sure! The miller's stomach is fast disappearing."

The cook, noticing his master's declining appetite, asked, "What's wrong with you that you won't eat?"

"Why should I tell you? You can't help me, and it was your prank that's to blame for my frightful situation," the miller said morosely.

But the cook was sure that he could help, and pestered the miller for an explanation while the unhappy man groaned and sighed until at last he unburdened his woes.

"Do you think the king would recognize you?" asked the cook.

"Why, no, I doubt it," answered the miller, taken aback by the question. He was even more taken aback when the cook declared, "It's a cinch! I'll go before the king in your place and answer the questions. If I lose my head it's my own fault. Lend me some of your clothes so they won't suspect anything."

From that moment the miller's appetite for meat and ruby wine returned, and he soon regained his usual rotundity.

On the appointed day the cook went to the court and was received by the king and his ministers. They were puzzled to see him arrive in the throne room panting under a heavy sack of flour.

"Well, can you tell me how many stars there are in the sky?" said the king.

"I've counted every last one, and for each star I put a grain of flour into this sack," replied the cook with a grin.

The king and his ministers looked at one another in astonishment, for how could they challenge the cook when none of them cared to count out every grain of flour?

So the king asked the second question. "How far is it from the earth to the heavens?"

The cook answered that readily enough. "Christ died about nine o'clock and entered heaven the same night, so from earth to the heavens is a journey of three hours at the most."

"How do you know he entered heaven the same night?" asked one of the ministers.

"Because he said to the thief on the left, 'Today you will be with me in paradise.'"

The king was surprised by this reply, and still

more curious to hear the other answers, so he continued his questions. "What is the king worth?"

"Christ was worth thirty pieces of silver. You come first after him on earth, so that makes you worth one coin less, or twenty-nine pieces of silver."

The king was even more impressed with such quick wit, but he believed the fourth question impossible to answer.

"What is the king thinking at this moment?"

The cook bowed very low and answered, "You are thinking that I am the miller, but in truth I am his cook."

The king and all his ministers roared with delight at the cook's cleverness. At last the king rose from his golden throne and said, "You have answered well, and since you are so much brighter than your master I wish and command that in all the kingdom you shall be known henceforth as the miller, while your master does the cooking." And he sent the cook home with a rich reward.

How the miller and his cook settled between them who was to be head of the mills and who was to rule in the kitchen, nobody knows. But the inscription written large on the wall of the house now is:

"THE TWO OF US LIVE WITHOUT
A CARE IN THE WORLD."

The Country was France. The Year, 1611. The King was ten years old. And this was what he had for dinner.

Corinth raisins in rose water.
Egg soupe with lemon juice, 20 spoonsful.
Broth, 4 spoonsful.
Cocks combs, 8.
A little boiled chicken.
4 mouthfuls of boiled veal.
The marrow of a bone.
A wing and a half of chicken, roasted and then fried in bread crumb.
13 spoonsful of jelly.
A sugar horn filled with apricots.
Half a sugared chestnut in rose water.
Preserved cherries.
A little bread and some fennel comfits.

The fennel comfits were for the little King's digestion.

# Clever Grethel

There was once a cook, and her name was Grethel. She wore shoes with red rosettes on them, and when she went walking in these shoes she would turn herself this way and that, saying: "Well I never, you *are* a handsome creature!"

At night as she combed her hair in the glass she would say: "My! so there you are!" And they called her "clever Grethel."

Whenever after a walk she came home to her master's house again, she would always take a little sippet of wine. "You see, Grethel, my dear, it makes the tongue able to *taste* better," she would say. "And what's a cook without a tongue?" In fact, Grethel kept her tongue very busy, nibbling and tasting.

Now one day her master said to her: "I have a guest coming this evening, Grethel, and a guest that knows what's what, and I want you to roast us a pair of fowls for supper. Two, mind you, young and tender. And I want 'em roasted to a turn."

Grethel said: "Why, yes, master. They shall taste so good you won't know what you're eating."

So she killed two fowls, scalded and plucked them, tucked in their legs with a little bit of liver in between, stuffed them with stuffing, and towards evening put them down to a clear, red fire to roast. She basted and basted them, and when they were done to a turn and smelt sweet as Arabia, and their breasts were a rich, clear, delicate brown, Grethel called out to her master:

"If that guest of yours don't come soon, master, I shall have to take the fowls away from the fire. And I warn you, they will be utterly spoilt, for they are just at their juiciest."

Her master said: "So, so! I will run out and see if he is coming."

As soon as her master had turned his back, Grethel thought to herself she would have another sip of something to drink. Having had one sip, she took another sip, and then another. Then she basted the fowls again, and twisted the spit. She puffed with the heat, the fire blazing in her face. Suddenly, as she stood looking at the fowls, she thought to herself:

"Now cooking's cooking! I shouldn't wonder if them birds taste as good as they smell. Oh, oh, oh! It's a sin. It's a shame!"

Then she looked out of the window; and when she saw that nobody was coming, she said to herself: "There! what did I tell you? And lawks! one of the wings is burning." So she cut off the wing with a twist of her sharp knife, and holding it between her finger and thumb, ate every scrap of it up, to the very bone.

Then, "Dear me," she sighed to herself, looking at the chicken, "that one wing left looks like another wing missing!" So she ate up the other. Then she took another sip of wine, and once more looked at the fowls.

"Now think what a sad thing," she said. "Once those two poor hens were sisters, and you couldn't tell 'em apart. But now look at them: one whole and the other nowt but legs!" So she gobbled up the wings of the other chicken to make the pair look more alike. And still her master did not come. Then said she to herself:

"Lor', Grethel, my dear, why worry? There won't be any guest to-night. He has forgotten all about it. And master can have some nice dry bread and cheese." With that she ate up completely one of the chickens, skin, stuffing, gravy and all, and then, seeing how sad and lonely the other looked all by itself with its legs sticking up in the air and both its wings gone, she finished off that too.

She was picking the very last sweet morsel off its wishbone when her master came running into the kitchen, and cried: "Quick, Grethel! Dish up! dish up! Our guest has just turned the corner."

At this moment she was standing in front of the fire in her fine shoes and great cooking apron, and she looked over her shoulder at her master. But he at once rushed out to see if the table was ready, and the wine on it; snatched up the great carving-knife, and began to sharpen it on the doorstep.

Pretty soon after, the guest came to the door and knocked. Grethel ran softly out, caught him by the sleeve, pushed him out of the porch, pressed her finger on her lips, and whispered: "Ssh! Ssh! on your life! Listen, now, and be off, I beseech you! My poor master has gone clean out of his senses at your being so late. Mad! mad! If he catches you, he will cut your ears off. Hark now! He is sharpening his knife on the doorstep!"

At this the guest turned pale as ashes, and hearing the steady rasping of the knife on the stone, ran off down the street as fast as his legs could carry him.

As soon as he was out of sight, Grethel hastened back
to her master.

"La, master!" she said, "*you've* asked a nice fine
guest to supper!"

"Why," says he, looking up with his knife in his
hand, "what's wrong with him?"

"Wrong!" says she. "Why, he had scarce put his
nose in at the door, when he gives a sniff. 'What!
chicken!' says he, 'roast chicken!' And away he
rushed into the kitchen, snatched up my two poor
beeootiful birds, and without even waiting for the
dish or the gravy, ran off with them down the street."

"What, *now?*" said her master.

"This very minute!" said Grethel.

"Both?" said her master.

"Both," said she.

"Heaven save us!" said her master. "Then I shall have nothing for supper!" And off he ran in chase of his guest, as fast as he could pelt, crying out as he did so:

"Hi, there! Stop! Stop! Hi! Just one! Just one! Only one!"

But the guest, hearing these words, and supposing that the madman behind him with his long knife meant one of his ears, ran on faster than ever into the darkness of the night.

And Grethel sat down, happy and satisfied. She gave one deep sigh, looked solemnly at the two bright red rosettes on her shoes, and had another sip or two of wine.

1 young chicken, whole, prepared for roasting
Vegetable oil or unsalted butter
Salt
Stuffing, if you wish. (Ready-made stuffing is good.)

Have the chicken at room temperature. Wipe it
with a slightly damp cloth. Sprinkle the body cavity
liberally with salt and loosely fill it with stuffing.
Draw the skin over the back and close the openings
by sewing with string, or insert skewers and lace
with string. Fold the wings back and press the tips
against the back. Press thighs close to body, tie the
ends of the legs together with string and bring it
down around the tailpiece, leaving two ends. Then
turn bird over on breast and bring each end of string
forward over the front and tip of one of the wings
and across the back to the other wing, and tie ends
securely in the middle of the back. Rub the entire
outside of the chicken with oil or soft unsalted butter. Place breast down in roasting pan. Roast in
moderate oven 325° to 350° F. until tender, allow-
ing 30 minutes per pound for an unstuffed bird; for
a stuffed bird, 40 minutes. When half done, turn
breast up and finish roasting. Baste frequently with

drippings in pan or with additional oil or melted butter. The chicken will be done when the joints of the leg can be moved easily and when the leg is pierced with a fork the juice runs clear with no trace of pink. Remove all string and skewers before serving.

\* \* \*

*As I walked through a field of wheat*
*I picked up something good to eat.*
*It was neither flesh, meat, nor bone*
*I kept it till it walked along.*

An egg which hatched into a chicken

# The One-Legged Crane

*The problem in this story is similar to the one in "Clever Grethel" but the cook resolves it in an entirely different way.*

There once lived in the city of Florence a very handsome and pleasure-loving prince called Corrado. Corrado loved to go hunting and after every hunt he loved to entertain his guests at a great banquet. Not only Corrado's lavish table, but the way the dishes were brought to it made him the talk of Florence. And what was the secret of the prince's unusual entertainment? I'll tell you. It was his cook.

Yes, Corrado had a marvelous cook who went by the strange name of Chichibio. But make no mistake about it. Chichibio was not just a cook. He was a kitchen poet; a culinary artist. Chichibio was never content merely to roast to a turn a wild boar, a partridge or a pheasant, and to serve it in the customary way. Oh no. Chichibio would create the game's natural setting on a huge platter, set the animal or fowl on it, surrounded by the miniature trees and plants, carry it proudly into the vast banquet hall, and finally place it on the long banquet table, enjoying to the full the cries of surprise and delight that greeted him. Sometimes the guests even clapped their hands and shouted, "Bravo! Bravo!" Chichibio would accept their applause and praise with a modest bow, while his master looked fondly on. The prince was very proud of Chichibio and considered himself extremely lucky to have such a talented cook.

Chichibio was not much to look at. His features were coarse and heavy, and he held his head a little to one side. No one would guess that he was a clever and quick-witted man as well as an excellent cook. But the twinkle in his eye belied the seeming dullness of his appearance, and those who knew him were aware of how shrewd he really was and what a genius he had for getting out of trouble.

Now listen to what happened one day and decide for yourself whether or not this was true.

On this particular day Corrado went hunting with

his favorite falcon and caught a young and beautiful crane. Cranes were a rare delicacy, so Corrado looked forward with pleasure to the banquet he planned for his guests that night. As soon as he returned from the hunt he called Chichibio to him, gave him the crane, and ordered him to prepare it in the most novel way he knew. Promising to outdo himself to please his master, Chichibio went back to the kitchen and set to work. As he plucked the crane and cleaned it and stuffed it, flavoring it with many fine herbs and spices brought to Italy from the Orient by the seafaring Venetian traders, Chichibio wracked his brain for an unusual idea. He wanted to present the crane as no crane had ever been presented before. Finally, the crane was set to roast on the spit. Soon after, such a delicious aroma filled the kitchen that Chichibio thought it was powerful enough to bring a dead man back to life.

Well, the aroma didn't quite do *that*, but it did bring to the kitchen door Brunetta, the pretty village girl with whom Chichibio was very much in love.

"Oh, Chichibio," cried Brunetta, "what *is* that heavenly smell? I was passing by and just had to stop. It absolutely drew me here."

Chichibio took her into the kitchen and showed

her the crane, roasting on the spit and sending out with every turn the most marvelous fragrance. Brunetta's mouth began to water. She came as close to the open fire as she dared. Pointing her finger at the fowl, she said, "I simply must have a leg of that crane."

Chichibio thought she was joking. He wagged his finger under her pert little nose, and playfully chanted: "You shall not have it from me. You shall not have it from me."

But Brunetta was not joking at all. The delicious aroma was more than she could bear; so, annoyed with Chichibio, she turned angrily on her heel, muttered "All right, if you care more about an old crane than about me," and started to leave the kitchen. The thought of losing Brunetta was more than Chichibio could bear, so he reached over, hastily tore off one of the crane's legs, and gave it to the girl. All smiles now, Brunetta snatched the crane's leg and greedily began to eat it.

Poor Chichibio! How could he serve a one-legged crane without anyone detecting the deception? He thought and thought and at last an idea came to him. He remembered that cranes, when asleep, stood on one leg. Chichibio decided to serve up a sleeping crane at the banquet that night.

And so he did. Before the astonished guests Chichibio set down a tremendous platter. Reeds and rushes had made of it a forest glade in the midst of which stood the crane on one leg, fast asleep. Corrado and all the guests burst into spontaneous applause. However, it did not take the prince long to discover that the crane had but one leg. He turned to Chichibio and demanded to know what had become of the other leg.

Chichibio feigned surprise. Opening his eyes very wide, he said, "The other leg? What other leg? Why, I always thought that cranes had only one leg."

Corrado did not wish to make a scene in front of his guests so he only said, "Indeed? We'll see about that in the morning."

At dawn the next day, the prince ordered Chichibio to mount up and accompany him in a search for some cranes. "I'd like you to prove to me that they have only one leg," he told his cook.

They had not gone very far when they came upon a beautiful shady meadow, with a lovely stream. It was an ideal spot for cranes to spend the night. As Corrado and Chichibio entered the glade, they saw several cranes in the stream, still asleep, and standing on one leg.

Chichibio, who had been shaking in his boots all the way, now drew a sigh of relief. "You can readily see, my lord," he said, "that I spoke the truth last night."

Too angry to answer, Corrado spurred his horse, rushed toward the cranes, and shouted, "Hoh! Hoh!" at the top of his lungs.

Startled, as was to be expected, the cranes put down their other leg and rose in sudden flight. Corrado galloped back to the quaking cook and demanded furiously, "How many legs do cranes have, Chichibio?"

"Two, my lord," Chichibio replied humbly. "I must have been mistaken."

"Then, Chichibio," thundered the prince, "where was our crane's other leg last night?"

Frightened as he was, Chichibio did not lose his wits. He looked up at his master and said, with an air of injured innocence, "Oh, but last night, my lord, you did not shout *Hoh! Hoh!* to the crane. If you had, it would most certainly have put down its other leg."

In spite of his anger, Corrado was so amused by Chichibio's answer that he burst into laughter and forgave his clever cook.

Monday last was brought from Howick to Berwick, to be shipp'd for London, for Sir Hen. Grey, Bart., a pie, the contents whereof are as follows: viz. 2 bushels of flour, 20 lb. of butter, 4 geese, 2 turkeys, 2 rabbits, 4 wild ducks, 2 woodcocks, 6 snipes, and 4 partridges; 2 neats' tongues, 2 curlews, 7 blackbirds, and 6 pigeons: it is supposed a very great curiosity was made by Mrs. Dorothy Patterson, housekeeper at Howick. It was near nine feet in circumference at bottom, weighs about twelve stone,* will take two men to present it to table; it is neatly fitted with a case, and four small wheels to facilitate its use to every guest that inclines to partake of its contents at table.

Item in "The Newcastle Chronicle" January 6, 1770.

* A stone equals 14 pounds.

# Pancake Day

*Pancake Tuesday is a very happy day*
*If you don't give us a holiday*
*We'll all run away.*

Shrove Tuesday is the day before Ash Wednesday and the beginning of the traditional Lenten fast. How it became known as Pancake Day happened in this way.

In 1445, a housewife in Olney, England, was making pancakes when the shriving bell rang, calling churchgoers to confession. The pancakes the housewife was making were to sustain her during her long wait at the church. The quick-thinking housewife snatched up her hot griddle and batter and hurried off to the church. And thus a new custom began.

On the morning of Shrove Tuesday, or Pancake Day as it is popularly called, the housewives of Olney gather at the village inn. Each housewife is wearing an apron over her dress and a scarf on her head and carrying a hot frying pan in her hand with a pancake in it ready for tossing. At the ringing of the bell each competitor tosses her pancake high in the air, catches it in her pan and starts on a quarter of a mile course, ending at the church. The pancake is tossed a second time on approaching the church and a third time at the church porch. The first competitor to arrive with her tossed pancake still in her pan is acclaimed the winner.

In 1950 the housewives of Liberal, Kansas, U.S.A., challenged the housewives of Olney, England, to a pancake race. The Olney housewives won—perhaps because they had had over five hundred years practice. This has become an annual event known as the International Pancake Day Race. Courses of identical length are set up in each country and times of winners are compared by transatlantic telephone. After the race everyone eats huge quantities of delicious pancakes.

In modern England people observe Pancake Day by eating these delicious little pancakes spread with jelly.

1 cup sifted flour
½ teaspoon salt
½ teaspoon grated lemon rind
4 eggs, separated
1 cup milk

Mix flour, salt and lemon rind. Beat egg yolks thoroughly and add with the milk to the dry ingredients. Beat batter until smooth. Beat egg whites until stiff and fold into batter.

Grease hot griddle or skillet with a little butter. Pour on a very thin layer of batter, making cakes about 5 inches in diameter. Bake until delicately browned on one side—about a minute. Turn and bake on the other side. Spread each pancake with jelly and roll up while hot. Makes about 12 pancakes.

For those who prefer breakfast pancakes served with butter and syrup, here is an American recipe:

## ✒ | FLY-OFF-THE-PLATE PANCAKES

1 cup sifted flour
¼ teaspoon salt
1 tablespoon sugar
1 tablespoon baking powder
1 egg
1 cup milk
2 rounded tablespoons dairy sour cream
2 tablespoons melted butter at room temperature

Sift dry ingredients into a mixing bowl. In another bowl beat egg, milk and sour cream. Pour into dry ingredients, beating with a slotted spoon or wire whisk to keep from lumping. Add butter and beat again until smooth.

Drop batter by tablespoonfuls onto hot, lightly greased griddle. Use 2 tablespoons of batter for each pancake. Let one side brown until golden. Turn and brown on other side. Serve with honey butter or syrup.

# HONEY BUTTER

1 cup honey
½ cup (1 stick) butter

Be sure both ingredients are at room temperature. Add honey slowly to softened butter and beat with a fork. Makes 1½ cups.

Serve cold or melt in top of double boiler and serve hot.

*A dish full of all kind of flowers,*
*You can't guess this riddle in two hours.*

Honey

# The Birth of Simnel Cake

*In England the fourth Sunday in Lent is called "Mothering Sunday." The custom of honoring one's mother on that particular day dates from the fifteenth century when children who had hired out as servants were given a holiday in mid-Lent so that they could return home to visit their parents. As an expression of love for their mothers and proof of their cooking skill they brought home a gift of "mothering" or "Simnel" cake. This was a very rich fruit cake: "The crust was made of flour, water and saffron, to envelop a filling of mixed plums, lemon peel and many good things. The edges were pinked, the top duly crisscrossed, the whole boiled in a cloth, then glazed with egg and finally baked." Nowadays Simnel cake is frequently made for Easter (and mother usually makes it). It is decorated with mar-*

*zipan rabbits, chickens, lambs, eggs, flowers, etc.*
*And this is how it came to be called Simnel cake.*

**B**oil it!' said Simon.
'Bake it!' said Nelly.
'You're wrong!' said he.
'I'm right!' said she.
'Take that!' said he.
'And that!' said she.
And so the quarrel began.

What was the quarrel about? A cake, my dears, no more and no less than a cake. And yet it started in a fit of loving-kindness. For Simon and Nelly, that ancient Shropshire goodman and his wife, were looking for their children to come gathering home as usual one Sunday when Lent was running out; and Nelly, a frugal soul, fetched the last of the unleavened dough to make a family cake.

'Plain fare,' said Simon.
'Too plain,' said Nelly.
'Plum-pudden?' said he.
'From Yule,' said she.
' 'Twould help,' said he.
'A lot,' said she.

And Nelly fetched the left-over Christmas pudding, and made a ball of the dough with the pudding inside. What a surprise for her boys and girls on Mothering Sunday! But how to cook this new sort of pudding-cake? Simon swore that a pudding should always be boiled; and Nelly vowed that a cake could only be baked; and very soon they were at it hammer and tongs. Nelly threw the wooden stool at Simon's wooden head, and Simon laid the stout besom across Nelly's buxom shoulders; and between them they managed to smash a bowl of eggs.

'Enough!' said Nelly.
'And more!' said Simon.
'Boil first,' said she.
'Bake second,' said he.
'You're right,' said she.
'And you,' said he.
And so the quarrel was mended.

Simon fed the fire with the stool and the besom, while Nelly glazed the cake with the broken yolks and whites; then the pudding-cake was boiled in the pot and baked in the oven, and so the first Mothering-Sunday-Cake was born.

So good it was that their children spread its fame, and christened it Sim-Nel on the spot; for (said they) such a cake should only be named after both its makers, who had conceived it in such perfect agreement.

'That's so!' said Sim.
'And *so!*' said Nell.
And as Simnel the cake is known to this very day.

*Modern Version*

For the filling and top:
1 8-ounce can almond paste
⅓ cup softened butter
1 egg white

Mash almond paste with fork. Add softened butter and egg yolk.
Mix together and beat well to blend.

For the cake:
½ cup (1 stick) butter
½ cup sugar
Grated rind of ½ lemon
3 eggs
1¾ cups sifted flour
1 teaspoon baking powder
½ teaspoon salt
1 teaspoon cinnamon
1 teaspoon ginger
1 teaspoon allspice
½ cup seedless dark raisins
½ cup seedless light raisins

½ cup currants
¼ cup glacé cherries, cut in half
¼ cup candied peel, sliced thin
¼ cup blanched almonds, chopped fine
Juice of ½ lemon

Cream the butter. Add the sugar and beat until fluffy and smooth. Add the grated lemon rind while you are beating. Whisk the eggs well and then beat them gradually into the sugar and butter, adding a little egg at a time and beating briskly after each addition until the mixture is smooth.

Sift together the flour, baking powder, salt and spices. Add gradually to the first mixture, combining thoroughly. Dredge the fruit with flour. Fold the fruit and almonds into the batter. Add lemon juice. Mix gently together.

Grease 9-inch round, deep cake tin, then line bottom and sides with heavy brown paper. Butter the paper.

Turn half the mixture into the cake tin. Spread half of the almond paste on top of the cake mixture. Add the remainder of the cake mixture and bake in a 300° F. oven for about 1¼ hours.

Remove cake from oven and cool. When cool, spread the remainder of the almond paste on top of the cake. Place in a 400° F. oven for 5 minutes to lightly brown the almond paste.

When cool, decorate with flowers, rabbits, Easter eggs, etc., molded from marzipan, if desired. (See recipe for marzipan on page 98.)

*Flour of England, fruit of Spain,*
*Met together in a shower of rain,*
*Put in a bag and tied round with a string,*
*If you'll tell me this riddle, I'll give you a*
  *ring.*

A plum pudding

# The Perambulatin' Pumpkin

**D**own in Beaverdam Valley the mountain folk had gathered for the county fair. Mr. Zeke Calloway held up a bulging pumpkin decorated with the blue ribbon for the first prize, and grinned triumphantly at his neighbor and rival, Mr. Hank Huggins.

"Reckon you don't grow pumpkins like that on your side of the mountain!" he crowed.

"Law me," drawled Hank who had been known on occasion to stretch the truth somewhat. "Law me, that little bitty thing would look like a peanut beside the pumpkins in my patch."

"Mighty funny thing you didn't bring any of your monstrous pumpkins to the fair," sniggered Zeke. "Mighty funny."

"Well, now, to tell you the truth I was aiming to

bring one but we had a little accident up in our place this morning. It broke up my plans somewhat."

"What kind of accident?" asked Zeke suspiciously.

"Well, you see it was this way: My wife had laid off to bring a pumpkin pie to the fair. She was up early baking the crust, and soon as it was done she climbed up the mountain to the field where the pumpkins were a-growing among the cornstalks.

"Of course all the pumpkins were too big and too heavy to carry, so she set out to cut a slab out of one, enough to make the filling for her pie.

"Seems she had trouble with that, too. Those pumpkins were so thick through that her arm wasn't long enough to reach into the inside where the juicy part was. But she was bound to get some of the very best part for she meant to take first prize with her pie. So what did she do but hack out a big hole and climb through it right into the center of that pumpkin.

"Now that would have been all right if the field where I planted 'em hadn't been so steep. But you know how it is—sometimes a pumpkin will break off the vine by its own weight and go rolling down the mountain.

"Well, you can just picture what happened when

that hefty wife of mine added her weight to the strain already on that vine. Before she knew what was happening, she was tumbling head over heels inside that pumpkin as it rolled out of the cornfield.

"I was in the barn lot hitching up the mule to the wagon when I looked up and saw it coming, a-picking up speed every minute. Before I could gather my wits to think what to do, it had hit the lot fence with a crash that sent the rails flying like matches. It tore through the barnyard, hit my wagon amidships, and sent the wheels flying four ways at once. The chickens and ducks ran squawking for their lives.

"I could hear my old lady screeching and hollering, 'Oh, my pie! my pie!' as she went reeling on down the mountain inside that pumpkin.

"Well, sir, there wasn't a thing I could do about it, so I figured there wasn't any use to get excited. I went to the ledge and looked after it a while as it went bumping and bounding down toward the valley, cutting a swath through the underbrush as it went.

"About halfway down I saw it bounce across the highway and crash into a covered wagon loaded with apples. Folks in the valley told me afterwards that apples rained down on 'em thick as hail for half an hour or so. They thought a miracle had happened up in the sky. Soon after that I lost sight of the thing, so I went on back to the barn.

"One look at my wagon told me I wasn't going to haul any pumpkins to the fair, but I didn't see any call to give up the trip. I could still go on mule-back. The pumpkin had headed in that direction anyhow, and I thought I might as well jog down and see what had happened to my wife.

"Into the cabin I went and put on my store-bought Sunday clothes. As I was on my way out again, my eyes lit on a piecrust sitting there on the kitchen table. It was nice and brown and crisp-looking and it came to me that this must have been what my wife was a-screeching about as she went rolling down the mountain. I picked it up, wrapped it carefully so it wouldn't break, and put it into my saddlebag.

"Then I straddled my mule and ambled on down the trail, wondering a mite as I jogged along where my old lady could have ended up.

"When I got down to Beaverdam I began to get a suspicion that she had rolled right onto the fair-ground. There was a hole in the side of the fence that would have accommodated an elephant, and the trail of wreckage inside the grounds looked like a hurricane had torn through. Folks were running

around like excited ants trying to fix up the damage.

"I followed the trail of ruin and at the end of it, sure enough, there sat my wife amidst the wreckage of the pumpkin. It had smashed against a stone chimney.

" 'Oh my pie, my pie! Now I've got no pie to take to the fair,' she was still a-wailing.

" 'Why, honey, yes you have,' I said to her as I rode up. I put my hand into my saddlebag and brought out the piecrust.

" 'But—but Hank,' she said. 'A pumpkin pie's

got to have sugar and eggs and spices and I don't know what-all.'

" 'Not this pumpkin, honey,' I said to her. 'The pumpkins I raise are flavored already. You just scoop out one of these pieces and spread it in the crust "as is," and you'll have a finer, tastier pie than anybody at the fair.'

"Well, sir, she got up from there, brushed herself off a mite, straightened her hair a little, and fixed up that pie just as I told her to. You can see for yourself what the upshot was.

"Look over there now, across that table full of wild strawberry jam beside that fancy patchwork quilt hanging on the wall. There she stands. See that pie she's a-holding? That's the very pie and if it hasn't got a blue ribbon a-hanging to it I'll eat my Sunday pants."

"Well, Hank," said Mr. Zeke Calloway, sourly, "all I've got to say is, it's too bad they're not offering prizes for tall tales. If they were there'd be two blue ribbons in your family."

1 envelope unflavored gelatin
⅔ cup sugar
½ teaspoon salt
½ teaspoon ginger
¼ cup water
3 eggs, separated
½ cup milk
1¼ cups canned pumpkin
½ cup heavy cream, whipped
Gingersnap Crumb Crust

In top part of double boiler mix gelatin, ⅓ cup sugar, salt and ginger. Stir in water, then beat in egg yolks one at a time. Add milk and stir over boiling water until gelatin is dissolved and mixture is slightly thickened. Remove from stove and stir in pumpkin. Cool.

Beat egg whites until stiff but not dry. Gradually add remaining ⅓ cup sugar and beat until very stiff. Fold in gelatin mixture and whipped cream. Turn into pie shell made of Gingersnap Crumb Crust. Chill until firm. Decorate with additional whipped cream if desired.

## ✒️ | GINGERSNAP CRUMB CRUST

Mix 1¼ cups fine crumbs (roll gingersnaps with rolling pin to make crumbs) and ¼ cup (½ stick) soft butter or margarine. Press into 9-inch piepan. Bake at 375° F. for 8 minutes.

*Round as an apple,*
*Yellow as gold,*
*With more things in it*
*Than you're years old.*

A pumpkin

# The Old Woman and the Tramp

There was once a tramp who went plodding his way through a forest. The distance between houses was so great that he had little hope of finding shelter before night set in. But all of a sudden he came upon a cottage with a fire burning on the hearth. How nice it would be to warm himself before that fire and to get a bite of something to eat, he thought!

Just then, an old woman opened the door.

"Good evening, and well met!" said the tramp.

"Good evening," said the woman. "Where do you come from?"

"South of the sun, and east of the moon," said the tramp. "And now I am on my way home again, for I have been all over the world except in this parish."

"You must be a great traveler," said the woman.

"What is your business here?"

"I would like shelter for the night."

"I thought as much," replied the woman, "but you may as well go away at once, for my place is not an inn."

"My good woman," pleaded the tramp, "you must not be so cross and hard-hearted. We are both human beings and should help one another."

"Help one another?" said the woman, "Help? Did you ever hear of such a thing? Who will help me, do you think? I haven't a morsel in the house! No, you'll have to look elsewhere for shelter."

But, like the rest of his kind, the tramp did not consider himself beaten at the first rebuff. Although the old woman grumbled and complained as loudly as she could, he was just as persistent. He kept on begging like a starved dog until at last she gave in, and he got permission to lie on the floor for the night.

That is very kind, he thought, and he thanked her.

"Better to lie on the floor without sleep than to suffer cold in the forest deep," he said. He was a merry fellow, this tramp, and was always ready with a rhyme.

When he entered the cottage he could see that the woman was not as badly off as she had pretended.

But she was a stingy woman of the worst sort, always complaining and grumbling.

The tramp made himself very agreeable and asked for something to eat.

"Where am I to get it?" demanded the woman. "I haven't tasted a morsel myself the whole day."

But the tramp was a cunning fellow, he was.

"Poor old granny, you must be starving," he said. "Well, well, I suppose I shall have to ask you to have something with me, then."

"Have something with *you!*" exclaimed the woman. "You don't look as if you could ask anyone to have anything! What have *you* to offer, I should like to know?"

"He who far and wide does roam sees many things not known at home; and he who many things has seen has wits about him and senses keen," said the tramp. "Better dead than lose one's head! Lend me a pot, granny!"

The old woman now became very curious, as you may guess, so she let him have a pot.

He filled the pot with water and put it on the fire. Then he blew with all his might till the fire was burning fiercely. He took a four-inch nail from his pocket, turned it three times in his hand and dropped it into the pot.

The woman stared with all her might.

"What is this going to be?" she asked.

"Nail broth," said the tramp, and began to stir the water with the porridge stick.

"Nail broth?" asked the woman.

"Yes, nail broth," said the tramp.

The old woman had seen and heard a good deal in her time, but that anybody could make broth with a nail, well, she had never heard the like of this before.

"That's something for poor people to know," she said, "and I should like to learn how to make it."

"That which is not worth having, will always go a-begging," said the tramp.

But if she wanted to learn how to make it she had only to watch him, he said, and went on stirring the broth.

The old woman squatted on the floor, her hands clasping her knees, and her eyes following the tramp's hand as he stirred the broth.

"This generally makes good broth," he said. "But this time it very likely will be rather thin, for this whole week I have been making broth with the same nail. If only I had a handful of sifted oatmeal to put in, that would make it all right," he said. "But what one has to go without, it's no use thinking more about," and so he stirred the broth again.

"Well, I think I have a scrap of flour somewhere,"

said the old woman. She went to fetch some, and it was both good and fine. The tramp began stirring the flour into the broth, and went on stirring while the woman sat staring now at him and then at the pot, unil her eyes nearly burst from their sockets.

"This broth would be good enough for company," the tramp said, putting in one handful of flour after another. "If only I had a bit of salted beef and a few potatoes to put in, it would be fit for gentle-folk, however particular they might be," he said. "But what one has to go without, it's no use think-ing more about."

When the old woman began to think it over, she thought she had some potatoes, and perhaps a bit of beef as well. These she gave to the tramp, who went on stirring, while the old woman sat and stared as hard as ever.

"This will be grand enough for the best in the land," he said.

"Well, I never!" said the woman. "And just fancy —all that with a nail!"

"If only we had a little barley and a drop of milk, we could ask the king himself to sup with us," the tramp said. "This is what he has every evening. That I know, for I have been in service under the king's cook."

"Dear me! Ask the king to have some! Well, I

never!" exclaimed the woman, slapping her knees. She was quite overcome by the tramp and his grand connections.

"But what one has to go without, it's no use thinking more about," said the tramp.

And then the woman remembered she had a little barley. And as for milk, well, she wasn't quite out of that, she said, for her best cow had just calved. She went to fetch both the one and the other.

The tramp went on stirring, and the woman sat staring, one moment at him and the next at the pot.

Suddenly the tramp took out the nail.

"Now it's ready, and we'll have a real feast," he said. "But with this kind of soup the king and the queen always have something to drink, and one sandwich at least. And then they always have a cloth on the table when they eat," he said. "But what one has to go without, it's no use thinking more about."

By this time the old woman had begun to feel quite grand, I can tell you. If that was all that was wanted to make it just as the king had it, she thought it would be nice to have it just the same way for once, and play at being king and queen with the tramp. She went straight to the cupboard and brought out a bottle of brandy and two glasses, butter and cheese, smoked beef and veal, until at last

the table looked as if it were decked out for company.

Never in her life had the old woman had such a grand feast, and never had she tasted such broth. Just fancy, made only with a nail!

She was in such a merry humor at having learned such an economical way of making broth that she could not do enough for the tramp who had taught her such a useful thing.

So they ate and drank, and drank and ate, until they could eat no more and both were tired and sleepy.

The tramp was ready to lie down on the floor to sleep. But that would never do, thought the old woman. No, that was impossible. "Such a grand person must have a bed to lie in," she said.

The tramp did not need much urging. "It's just like the sweet Christmas time. Happy are they who meet such good people," he said. And he lay down on the bed and went to sleep.

Next morning when he awoke the old woman had coffee ready for him. And as he was leaving she pressed a shiny coin in his hand.

"Thanks, many thanks, for what you have taught me," she said. "Now I shall live in comfort, since I have learned how to make broth with a nail."

"Well, it isn't very difficult, if one only has something good to add to it," said the tramp as he went on his way.

The woman stood at the door staring after him.

"Such people don't grow on every bush," she said.

3 or 4 pounds meaty soupbones (beef or veal shank)
or 2 pounds stewing chuck

1 pound can stewed tomatoes

1 cup chopped parsley

1 cup chopped celery leaves

1 teaspoon salt

¼ teaspoon pepper

½ teaspoon each of marjoram, thyme, savory, or any
one of these herbs

1 garlic clove, crushed, or ½ teaspoon garlic powder

3 cups uncooked vegetables, such as one-inch potato
cubes, diced carrots, diced green peppers, sliced
onion, sliced celery, cut green beans

Put soupbones or meat into a pot containing tomatoes and 2 quarts of water.

Add parsley, celery leaves, salt, pepper, herbs and garlic.

Bring to a boil, then turn down heat and simmer until meat is tender (3 to 4 hours).

If soupbones are used, remove bones from broth, remove meat and marrow from bones, and add them to broth.

Add vegetables.

Taste, and add more salt and pepper if needed.

Boil gently until vegetables are tender (about 20 minutes).

What stands on one leg with its heart in its head?

A cabbage

# Index of Recipes

BUTTER COOKIES | 27

CHERRY DUMPLINGS | 39

CHOCOLATE BUTTER ICING | 88

CHOCOLATE POTATO CAKE | 87

COCONUT KISSES | 100

ENGLISH SIMNEL CAKE | 134

FAIRY CAKE | 25

GINGERSNAP CRUMB CRUST | 144

GRIDDLE BREAD | 55

HEARTY SOUP | 153

HONEY BUTTER | 129

MARZIPAN | 98

MOLASSES MILK SHAKE | 89

PANCAKES (2 recipes) | 127, 128

PUMPKIN CHIFFON PIE | 143

ROAST CHICKEN | 115

Ellin Greene says, "One of my favorite pastimes is browsing through cookery books. Another is telling stories to boys and girls. Perhaps because of these joint interests, I especially enjoy telling stories about cooks or stories in which food plays a vital role. Or perhaps the reason goes back even farther—to my childhood. One of my warmest memories is afternoon tea, when my English-born mother would amuse me with stories from her own childhood—stories that had their foundation in the rich folklore of Herefordshire."

Trina Schart Hyman is the gifted young illustrator of numerous books for children and has also written one herself. The books she has illustrated include *The Pumpkin Giant* and *Princess Rosetta and the Popcorn Man,* which were also published by Lothrop.

She enjoys outdoor sports and the country setting of Lyme, New Hampshire, where she lives with her daughter.